THE COMPLETE ORGAN PLAYER SONGBOOK VOLUME 1

Arranged by Kenneth Baker

G000134570

Contents

Wise Publications
London/New York/Sydney/Cologne

Exclusive Distributors:
Music Sales Limited
78 Newman Street, London W1P 3LA, England
Music Sales Corporation
24 East 22nd Street, NY 10010, New York, USA
Music Sales Pty. Limited
27 Clarendon Street, Artarmon, Sydney, NSW 2064, Australia

This book © copyright 1982 by
Wise Publications
ISBN 0.7119.0044.2
Order No. AM 30511

**Teacher & Student's Guide to the
Complete Organ Player**
This excellent guide written by
Kenneth Baker contains valuable notes
to the nine books of the Complete Organ
Player Course. It is available from
Music Sales Limited, 78 Newman Street, London W1P 3LA.
For your free copy, please send 25p in stamps
to cover postage and handling.

Music Sales complete catalogue lists thousands of titles
and is free from your local music book shop, or direct from
Music Sales Limited. Please send 25p in stamps for postage to
Music Sales Limited, 78 Newman Street, London W1P 3LA.

J.B. Offset Printers (Marks Tey) Limited, Marks Tey.

REGISTRATION TABLE
(For All Organs)

GENERAL ELECTRONIC ORGANS

(1) Upper: Flute 8', 4'
      Lower: Flute 8', 4'
      Pedal: 8'
      Vibrato: On (or Leslie: Tremolo)

(2) Upper: Trumpet 8'
      Lower: Flute 8', 4'
      Pedal: 8'
      Vibrato: On

(3) Upper: Clarinet 8'
      Lower: Flute 8', 4'
      Pedal: 8'
      Vibrato: On (or Off)

(4) Upper: Violin (String) 8'
      Lower: Flute 8', String 4'
      Pedal: 8'
      Vibrato: On

(5) Upper: Trumpet 8', Flute 8', 4'
      Lower: Flute 8', String 8'
      Pedal: 8'
      Vibrato: On (or Leslie: Tremolo)

(6) Upper: Flute 16', 8', 4', 2'
      Lower: Flute 8', 4', String 8'
      Pedal: 16' + 8'
      Vibrato: On (or Leslie: Tremolo)

(7) Upper: Flute 16', 8', 2', String 8'
      Lower: Flute 8', Horn 8'
      Pedal: 16' + 8'
      Vibrato: On (or Leslie: Tremolo)

(8) Upper: Flute 8', 4', Clarinet 8'
      Lower: Synthesized Strings
                  (or Flute 8', String 8')
      Pedal: 8'
      Vibrato: On (or Leslie: Tremolo)

DRAWBAR ORGANS

(1) Upper: 00 7600 000
      Lower: (00) 6704 000(0)
      Pedal: 4 – (2)
      Vibrato: On (or Leslie: Tremolo)

(2) Upper: 00 7877 420
      Lower: (00) 6805 000(0)
      Pedal: 5 – (3)
      Vibrato: On

(3) Upper: 00 7272 420
      Lower: (00) 7702 000(0)
      Pedal: 4 – (2)
      Vibrato: On (or Off)

(4) Upper: 00 5666 654
      Lower: (00) 6543 211(0)
      Pedal: 4 – (2)
      Vibrato: On

(5) Upper: 00 8864 321
      Lower: (00) 6333 222(0)
      Pedal: 4 – (3)
      Vibrato: On (or Leslie: Tremolo)

(6) Upper: 60 8806 004
      Lower: (00) 6504 332(0)
      Pedal: 6 – (3)
      Vibrato: On (or Leslie: Tremolo)

(7) Upper: 60 8557 520
      Lower: (00) 5665 321(0)
      Pedal: 5 – (3)
      Vibrato: On (or Leslie: Tremolo)

(8) Upper: 00 8783 603
      Lower: (00) 5654 432(0)

      Pedal: 4 – (2)
      Vibrato: On (or Leslie: Tremolo)

Sloop John B

Words & Music: Brian Wilson

Registration No. ⑤
Suggested Drum Rhythm: Bossa Nova

♩ = 96

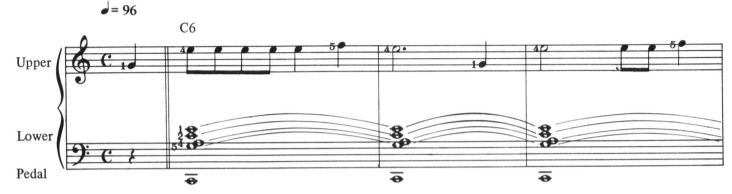

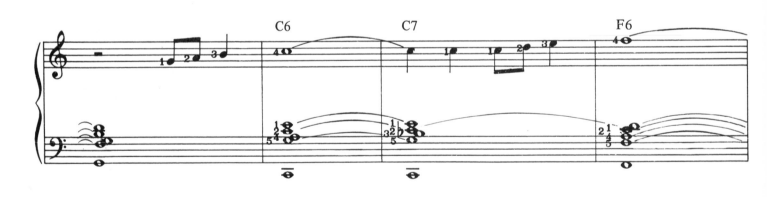

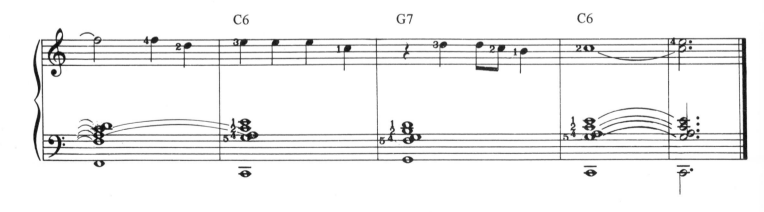

She'll Be Coming 'Round The Mountain

Traditional

Registration No. ⑦
Suggested Drum Rhythm: Swing

A Gordon For Me

Words & Music: Robert Wilson

Registration No. ⑧
Suggested Drum Rhythm: Waltz

♩ = 100   VERSE

Let Him Go, Let Him Tarry

Traditional

Mary's Boy Child

Words & Music: Jester Hairston

Registration No. ④
Suggested Drum Rhythm: Bossa Nova

Rivers Of Babylon

Words & Music: Farian, Reyam, Dowe & McMaughton

Registration No. ⑥
Suggested Drum Rhythm: Rock

♩= 112
CHORUS

Streets Of London

Words & Music: Ralph McTell

I Love You Because

Words & Music: Leon Payne

Registration No. ④
Suggested Drum Rhythm: Rhumba (or Shuffle, or Swing)

Smile

Words: John Turner & Geoffrey Parsons. Music: Charles Chaplin

Amazing Grace

Traditional

Registration No. ②
Suggested Drum Rhythm: Waltz

♩ = 80

Aloha Oe

Traditional

Registration No. ③
Suggested Drum Rhythm: Swing

Fare - well to thee, fare - well, fare - well, The sigh - ing winds will ech - o this re - frain Our love so deep in fon - dest mem - 'ry keep, Un - til we meet a - gain.

Annie's Song

Words & Music: John Denver

Far Away Places

Words & Music: Joan Whitney & Alex Kramer

call - in', me. I'm 'bout in a

book that I took from a shelf_____ I

start get - tin' rest - less when - ev - er I hear the

whis - tle of a train_____ I

pray for the day I can get un - der way and

Galway Bay

Words & Music: Dr Arthur Colahan

Registration No. ②
Suggested Drum Rhythm: No Drums

Shadow Waltz

Words & Music: Al Dubin & Harry Warren

Registration No. ④
Suggested Drum Rhythm: Waltz

♩ = 92

In the sha-dows let me come and sing to you.

Let me dream a song that I can bring to

you. _____ Take me in your arms and

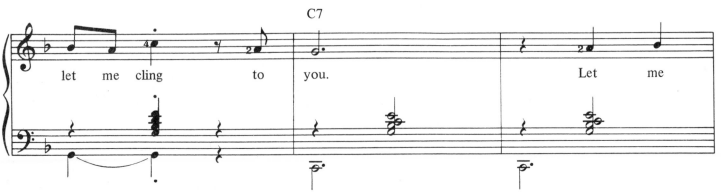

let me cling to you. Let me

As Long As He Needs Me

Words & Music: Lionel Bart

Registration No. ⑥
Suggested Drum Rhythm: Swing (or Bossa Nova)

♩ = 76

Can't Smile Without You

Words & Music: Chris Arnold, David Martin & Geoff Morrow

Registration No. ⑧
Suggested Drum Rhythm: Swing

♩ = 104

Hasta Manana

Words & Music: Benny Andersson, Stig Anderson & Bjorn Ulvaeus

Registration No. ⑥
Suggested Drum Rhythm: Swing

Alone Again (Naturally)

Words & Music: Raymond O'Sullivan

Registration No. ②
Suggested Drum Rhythm: Rock

♩ = 108

On The Sunny Side Of The Street

Words: Dorothy Fields. Music: Jimmy McHugh

Registration No. ⑧
Suggested Drum Rhythm: Swing

Raindrops Keep Falling On My Head

Words: Hal David. Music: Burt Bacharach

Registration No. ⑤
Suggested Drum Rhythm: Swing

♩ = 118

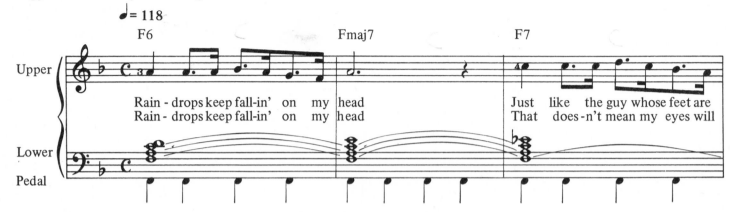

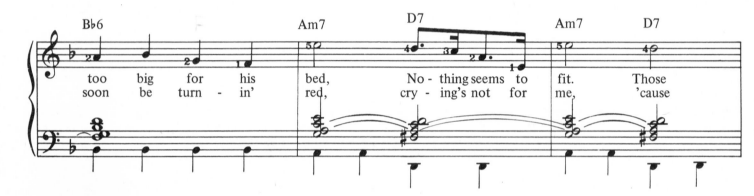

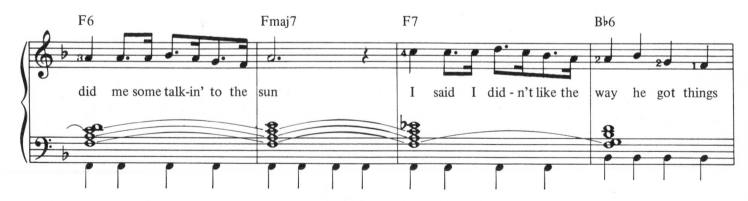

D.C. al Coda

♦ *CODA*

I Write The Songs

Words & Music: Bruce Johnston

A Swingin' Safari

Music: Bert Kaempfert

Registration No. ⑤
Suggested Drum Rhythm: Swing

♩ = 120

She Loves You

Words & Music: John Lennon & Paul McCartney

Registration No. ⑦
Suggested Drum Rhythm: Rock

* High C

CHORD CHART (For Left Hand)

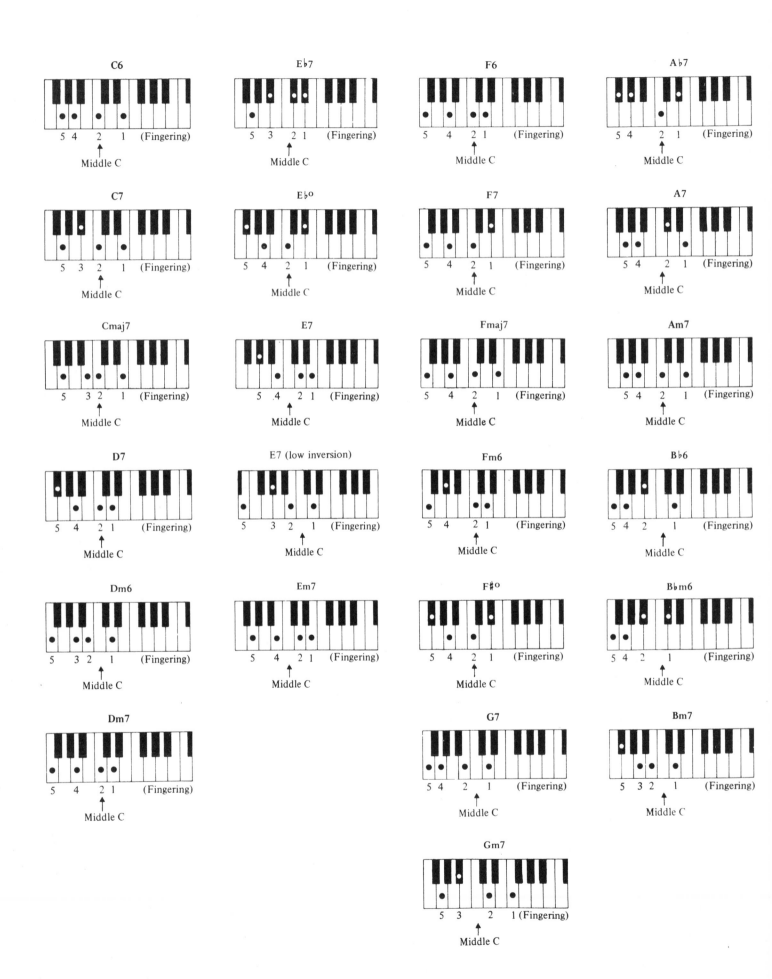

Oxford **Mathematics**
Primary Years Programme

2

Contents

OXFORD
UNIVERSITY PRESS
AUSTRALIA & NEW ZEALAND

Unit 1 Number and place value

Topic 1 Place value

Student Book pages 2–5

Learning focus

Read, write, represent and order whole numbers up to hundreds

Materials

- base-10 blocks
- abacuses (optional)
- items for counting, e.g. playing cards, pictures from magazines, counters
- craft sticks bundled into tens and ones
- small whiteboards and markers
- town population websites
- *BLM 1: Hundreds, tens and ones chart*
- *Activity sheet 1: Sunshine and rainfall*

Potential difficulties: Recording numbers

Some students have difficulty with the concept of zero as a placeholder in larger numbers, e.g. writing one hundred and three as 103.

- Through games, reinforce the idea that hundreds numbers have three digits. Give students the opportunity to discuss and manipulate numbers that they encounter in everyday life.
- Use hundreds, tens and ones charts, and manipulatives, such as base-10 blocks or an abacus, to show students the composition of numbers in different ways.

Daily practice activity

Choose a daily mystery number and give students clues based on place value. Use different combinations, such as "I have 1 hundred and 3 ones" or "I have 10 tens and 3 ones". Then ask students to discuss or write down what they think the number is.

Session 1: Pre-assessment

Students to complete: Pre-test 1, Unit 1, Topic 1, p. 64.

Session 2: Topic introduction

WHOLE CLASS

Introductory activity: Making a hundred

In pairs or small mixed-ability groups, ask students to assemble a collection of 100 items such as counters, pictures from magazines or playing cards. Invite each group to share their collection with the class, focusing on how they know they have 100, and how they grouped and counted their items. Extend students' thinking by asking them to suggest how they would approach the activity if they had to make 1000, drawing on place value language such as "hundreds", "tens" and "ones" during the discussion.

AT-STANDARD GROUP

Student Book

Students to complete: Guided and Independent Practice activities, pp. 2–4. Ask early finishers to make as many different 3-digit numbers as they can, using the digits in question 4, p. 4.

SUPPORT GROUP

Concept exploration and skill development: Place value practice

Allocate pairs of students a 2-digit number and ask them to write it on *BLM 1: Hundreds, tens and ones chart*. Students then make the number using craft sticks bundled into tens and ones. Discuss with students what each digit in their number means, e.g. the 2 in 28 is 2 tens. Repeat until you feel students are ready to try the same activity with 3-digit numbers.

Student Book with teacher support

Students to complete: Guided Practice activities, p. 2. Ask students to use concrete materials to make the numbers to support their understanding.

EXTENSION GROUP

Student Book

Students to complete: Guided and Independent Practice activities, pp. 2–4.

Activity sheet

Students to begin: *Activity sheet 1: Sunshine and rainfall*.

OXFORD UNIVERSITY PRESS

Session 3: Instruction and consolidation

WHOLE CLASS

Topic exploration: Understanding place value

It's important for students to develop a solid understanding of the concept that the place of a digit within a number determines its size. Write down two 3-digit numbers with different digits in the hundreds column, but don't show the class initially. Tell students they must work out whether the first or the second number is larger by only showing them one digit. Ask them if they would like to see the hundreds, tens or ones digit, and why. Once students know that the hundreds digit is the key, reverse the game and ask them to find the smaller of the two numbers. Do they know that the hundreds digit is still the one they need, or do they associate the word "smaller" with the ones digit? Extend students' thinking by choosing numbers with the same digit in the hundreds column and exploring how to work out which is larger.

AT-STANDARD GROUP

Teacher activity: Partitioning numbers

The ability to manipulate numbers into different combinations of hundreds, tens and ones is important for more advanced mental and written calculation skills.

Provide each student with a small whiteboard and marker to play *Number survivor*. Start with a simple clue, such as "I have 1 hundred, 3 tens and 5 ones", and ask students to write the numbers in numerals. Students should then display what they have written, and any students who wrote the numbers incorrectly are out of the game. Continue giving students clues, making them harder by introducing more complex combinations, such as "I have 1 hundred, 13 tens and 8 ones". If necessary, use base-10 blocks to model the numbers so students can consolidate their understanding with the support of visual representation.

Student Book

Students to complete: Extended Practice activities, p. 5.

SUPPORT GROUP

Student Book with teacher support

Students to complete: Independent Practice activities, pp. 3–4. As a group, check the answers to the Independent Practice activities, modelling with concrete materials if necessary to support understanding, before moving on to the Extended Practice tasks.

EXTENSION GROUP

Student Book

Students to complete: Extended Practice activities, p. 5.

Activity sheet

Students to complete: *Activity sheet 1: Sunshine and rainfall*

Session 4: Instruction and consolidation

WHOLE CLASS

Topic exploration: Number profile

Individually or in pairs (mixed- or like-ability), ask students to choose a number to profile. The profile should include everything they know about the number, such as how many digits it has, different ways to rename it and examples of where to find the number, e.g. on a bus or as a page number. It should also include a visual representation of the number. The finished work can be shared within the class, or even at an assembly, and displayed around the classroom.

Topic exploration: Numbers in action

Ask students what a town is and how it is different from a city. In pairs, challenge students to use the internet to find towns with populations of fewer than 1000 people. Students should order the populations of at least five of the towns from smallest to largest, and write the total population in figures, words and expanded notation. Students then choose one of the towns and write a short, illustrated description of it, including the population and any other relevant figures, for display in the classroom.

Practice and Mastery Book

The Practice and Mastery Book can be used as a homework activity or during class time. The Practice activities support the Independent Practice activities in the Student Book; the Challenge activities support the Extended Practice activities in the Student Book; and the Mastery activities allow students to demonstrate their proficiency by applying their knowledge in open-ended and/or real-life problem-solving contexts.

Session 5: Post-assessment

Students to complete: Post-test 1, Unit 1, Topic 1, p. 65.

Unit 1 Number and place value

Topic 2 Adding in your head

Student Book pages 6–10

Learning focus

Describe and choose mental strategies for addition of 2-digit numbers

Materials

- class hundred chart (or *BLM 10: Hundred chart*)
- playing cards, counters, 10-frames, 6-sided dice
- online interactive number line
- blank cards for students to write on
- base-10 blocks (optional)
- *Activity sheet 2: What do you think?*

Activity sheet materials

- a digital tablet (optional)

Potential difficulties: Number fact recall

To use mental strategies effectively, students need to be fluent with basic number facts.

- Ensure that students are confident with addends to 10 and can express these in both addition and subtraction contexts. Extend this knowledge by helping students relate it to larger numbers. For example, if they know that 6 + 4 = 10, they also know that 60 + 40 = 100.
- Use similar strategies with other basic number facts such as doubles.

Daily practice activity

Point to a number on a hundred chart and ask students to identify what is 10 more and 20 more than the number. Repeat this each day with a range of different numbers.

Session 1: Pre-assessment

Students to complete: Pre-test 2, Unit 1, Topic 2, p. 66.

Session 2: Topic introduction – Adding with doubles

WHOLE CLASS

Introductory activity: Doubles or near doubles snap

Split students into pairs. Give them a pack of playing cards with the face cards removed. Ask the students to turn over a card and mentally double the number, then call out the answer. The first student to correctly call out the doubled number scores a point. As students become proficient, have them mentally double the number and add one, or double the number and add two.

Introductory activity: Approximate and exact answers

Near doubles problems provide a good platform to discuss when students need to find the exact answer to a problem and when an approximation will suffice. Put forth the scenario that a group of five students and a group of six students want to go to the city in a minibus. Would it be important to find the exact total of students going? Why or why not? Invite the students to suggest ways to calculate the approximate and exact totals using mental addition strategies. Next, suggest that the same groups decided to go to the city by train. Would an approximate total be acceptable in this scenario? Does this change the importance of making an accurate calculation?

In small groups, ask students to think of addition situations where it might not be necessary to know the exact total, and suggest strategies they could use to make approximate calculations. Then have students do the same with scenarios that require accurate answers. Share their responses as a class, clarifying anything students are unsure of.

AT-STANDARD AND EXTENSION GROUPS

Student Book

Students to complete: Guided and Independent Practice activities, pp. 6–7. Ask early finishers to play *Doubles snap* with a partner.

SUPPORT GROUP

Concept exploration and skill development: Adding with doubles

Divide students into pairs and give each student some counters and a 10-frame. Ask each of them to put six counters on a 10-frame. How many counters

OXFORD UNIVERSITY PRESS

do they have between them? Get students to move all their counters together on the 10-frames to check their answer. Repeat with other numbers to practise doubles facts, allowing students to see the totals on the 10-frames each time.

Student Book with teacher support

Students to complete: Guided Practice activities, p.6.

Session 3: Topic introduction – Getting to a 10

WHOLE CLASS

Introductory activity: Adding numbers to tens

Divide students into pairs and, at the onset, remind them that it's easier to add numbers to tens. Ask the first student to roll a dice and put that number of counters on a 10-frame. The second student must then determine how many more counters are needed to get to the next 10 – before having their turn at rolling the dice. Once they've rolled, ask them to add that number of counters to the 10-frames. Set a target, such as 50 or 100, and continue until that target number is reached.

AT-STANDARD AND EXTENSION GROUPS

Student Book

Students to complete: Guided and Independent Practice activities, pp. 8–9. Ask early finishers to play *Adding numbers to tens* with a specific target that isn't a multiple of 10, e.g. 86. At each turn, ask students to identify how many more counters are needed to get to the next 10 and to the target number.

SUPPORT GROUP

Concept exploration and skill development: Interactive number lines

Access an online interactive number line. Tell students they are going to add 7 to 17. Start at 17 and then click on the next 10. Ask: "How many have been added so far? How many more still need to be added? What do you think the total will be?"

Ask students to add the remaining 4 on the number line to find the total. Repeat with other numbers.

Student Book with teacher support

Students to complete: Guided Practice activities, p. 8.

Session 4: Instruction and consolidation

WHOLE CLASS

Topic exploration: Which strategy?

List four addition problems on the board, such as 8 + 9, 18 + 5, 29 + 7 and 13 + 12. In pairs, ask students to discuss whether the near doubles strategy or the getting-to-a-10 strategy would be more effective for each one. Could either be used? Share some responses and the answers as a class.

AT-STANDARD GROUP

Teacher activity: Addition card calculator

First, divide students into pairs and give them five blank cards. Ask them to write a "2-digit plus 2-digit" addition problem on each one. Give students enough time to come up with five different addition problems and encourage them to discuss any challenging number combinations.

Next, sit students in a circle and choose one student to be the first calculator. The calculator stands behind another student and one of the addition cards is held up. If the calculator answers correctly first, they score a point and move behind the next student to the left of the circle. If the student sitting in the circle answers first, he or she trades places with the calculator and moves behind the next student to the left. Ask students to verbalise how they got their answers and make a note of any students who are struggling with particular strategies.

Student Book

Students to complete: Extended Practice activities, p. 10.

SUPPORT GROUP

Student Book with teacher support

Students to complete: Independent Practice activities, pp. 7 and 9, and Extended Practice activities, p. 10. As a group, check the answers to the Independent Practice activities, modelling any areas of difficulty using concrete materials, such as 10-frames or base-10 blocks. If students are ready, support them to complete the Extended Practice activities, modelling examples as appropriate.

EXTENSION GROUP

Student Book

Students to complete: Extended Practice activities, p. 10.

Activity sheet

Students to complete: Activity sheet 2.

Practice and Mastery Book

See p. 3 for information about how to use the Practice and Mastery Book activities.

Session 5: Post-assessment

Students to complete: Post-test 2, Unit 1, Topic 2, p. 67.

Unit 1 Number and place value
Topic 3 Exploring addition
Student Book pages 11–16

Learning focus

Describe and choose written strategies for addition of 2-digit numbers

Materials

- dice
- length of thin rope or twine and different coloured pegs
- 10-frames
- counters
- playing cards
- *BLM 2: Number lines 0–20*
- *Activity sheet 3: Selling chocolates*

Potential difficulties: Understanding the concept of addition

Students may find the concept of addition difficult to understand, so they shouldn't be pushed from the concrete to the abstract too quickly.

- Conduct oral activities that allow students to articulate their thinking, using manipulatives to give visual reinforcement.
- Encourage students to make predictions about results of addition to ensure they understand that the answer will be bigger than the addends. Again, provide support with concrete materials when testing predictions.

Daily practice activity

On the first day, brainstorm all the words and symbols that students associate with addition. Draw on these to solve a simple addition problem each day, such as 15 + 9 = _____. Record the problem and answer in as many different ways as possible, e.g. record it on the interactive whiteboard, on a number line, as a horizontal number sentence, or by using materials.

Session 1: Pre-assessment

Students to complete: Pre-test 2, Unit 1, Topic 3, p. 66.

Session 2: Topic introduction – Adding on a number line

WHOLE CLASS

Introductory activity: Comparing written strategies

Present students with a problem in context. For example, say: On our next excursion, one bus will hold 34 students and the other will hold 42 students. How many students are there altogether?

In mixed-ability pairs, ask students to represent the problem and answer in as many ways as possible. Before they start, brainstorm recording options with students, such as number lines, 10-frames and horizontal addition. Providing students with a range of ideas allows them to find the method that best suits them. Allow time to share the responses when the students have completed the activity in order to develop a bank of different recording methods.

AT-STANDARD AND EXTENSION GROUPS

Student Book

Students to complete: Guided, Independent and Extended Practice activities, pp. 11–13. Ask early finishers to choose a target number and find different combinations of numbers that add together to make that number, modelling it on an empty number line.

SUPPORT GROUP

Concept exploration and skill development: "Counting on" practice

Use *BLM 2: Number lines 0–20* to model counting on. In a group, roll a single dice and ask a student to circle that number on a number line. Roll again and choose another student to predict what number will be reached by counting on by the number rolled. Check on the number line. Repeat until the number 20 or more is reached. Ask students to play again following this process on their own number lines to see who reaches 20 first.

Student Book with teacher support

Students to complete: Guided Practice activities, p. 11. Discuss with students which number to start from and why.

OXFORD UNIVERSITY PRESS

Session 3: Topic introduction – You can add numbers in any order

WHOLE CLASS

Introductory activity: Changing adding order

Choose two students to hold a length of thin rope or twine across the front of the classroom. Put two pegs of one colour on one end of the line and three of another colour on the other end and ask students to tell you how many pegs you have in total. Write this as 2 + 3 = 5 on the board. Ask the students holding the line to change ends so that the line is rotated and the coloured pegs are now in the opposite order. Can students see that there are still 5 pegs? Write the new equation on the board. Repeat with different numbers, eventually adding a third number to show students that the order you add in won't change the total.

AT-STANDARD GROUP

Student Book

Students to complete: Guided, Independent and Extended Practice activities, pp. 14–16. Ask early finishers to choose any three numbers and write three addition sums using the numbers in different orders.

SUPPORT GROUP

Student Book with teacher support and concrete materials

Students to complete: Guided and Independent Practice activities, pp. 11, 12, 14 and 15. Work through the Guided Practice activities, using 10-frames and counters to model the problems. Once complete, support students to model the Independent Practice activities, then ask them to complete the activities themselves.

EXTENSION GROUP

Student Book

Students to complete: Guided, Independent and Extended Practice activities, pp. 14–16.

Activity sheet

Students to complete: *Activity sheet 3: Selling chocolates.*

Session 4: Instruction and consolidation

WHOLE CLASS

Topic exploration: Commutative property on a number line

To reinforce the idea that numbers can be added in any order, draw a number line from 0 to 20 on a whiteboard and write an equation with three small addends, e.g. 2 + 5 + 4. Invite students to estimate what the answer is likely to be and then ask a student to demonstrate the "jumps" for the equation using one colour. Rearrange the addends and ask students to predict what they think the answer will be. Invite a second student to represent the jumps using a different colour. Is the answer the same? As a class or in small groups, test the theory with larger numbers using a number line, and reinforce it using concrete materials where appropriate.

AT-STANDARD AND EXTENSION GROUPS

Teacher activity: Making 2-digit numbers

In pairs, give students a deck of playing cards with the face cards removed. Ask them to draw out four cards to form two 2-digit numbers. Get students to work together to add the two numbers, using and recording a strategy of their choice. Students can repeat the activity with new numbers or with 3-digit numbers as appropriate. Allow time for groups to share the strategies they used.

SUPPORT GROUP

Student Book with teacher support

Students to complete: Extended Practice activities, pp. 13 and 16. Ask students to form pairs and check each other's answers. Where there is disagreement, encourage students to talk through the strategy to try to agree on the correct response. Share responses and strategies as a group.

Practice and Mastery Book

See p. 3 for information about how to use the Practice and Mastery Book activities.

Session 5: Post-assessment

Students to complete: Post-test 2, Unit 1, Topic 3, p. 67.

Unit 1 Number and place value
Topic 4 Subtracting in your head

Student Book pages 17–21

Learning focus

Describe and choose mental strategies for subtraction of 2-digit numbers

Materials

- class hundred chart (or *BLM 10: Hundred chart*)
- counters
- 10-frames
- two 6-sided dice
- interlocking cubes of different colours
- two different coloured sets of counters
- online interactive number line
- *BLM 3: Subtraction think board*
- *BLM 4: Four in a row*
- *Activity sheet 4: Subtraction race*

Activity sheet materials

- two 6-sided dice

Potential difficulties: Introducing the subtraction symbol

It's important that students understand what "taking away" or "subtraction" means before the formal subtraction symbol is used.

- Model subtraction problems on 10-frames using the language of subtraction. Match this with a formal equation only when students are confident with the concepts.
- Use modelled scenarios, oral reasoning and written problems to ensure students understand the different applications of subtraction, e.g. "take away", "difference between" and "finding the missing part in equations". Link the subtraction symbol to these applications only when students are confident.

Daily practice activity

Point to a number on a hundred chart and ask students to tell you what is 1 less, 5 less, 10 less and 20 less than the number. Repeat this each day with a new starting number.

Session 1: Pre-assessment

Students to complete: Pre-test 3, Unit 1, Topic 4, p. 68.

Session 2: Topic introduction – Getting to a 10

WHOLE CLASS

Introductory activity: Getting to a 10

Divide students into pairs and give them counters and two 10-frames. Ask them to put 14 counters on the frames. How many do they need to take away from 14 to make 10? Write the problem on the board in words and using the subtraction symbol. Now that students know 14 take away 4 is 10, ask them to predict what 14 take away 5 is, then show it on the 10-frames. Repeat with different numbers to practise getting to a 10.

AT-STANDARD AND EXTENSION GROUPS

Student Book

Students to complete: Guided and Independent Practice activities, pp. 17–18. Ask early finishers to get into pairs and roll two dice to form a 2-digit number. They need to identify how many they would need to subtract to get to the nearest 10 and what number they will reach.

SUPPORT GROUP

Concept exploration and skill development: Think boards

Ask students to make a tower of 10 interlocking cubes of one colour and six of another. How many do they have altogether? How many do they need to take away to make 10? Give students *BLM 3: Subtraction think board* and ask them to write the problem (e.g. 16 take away 6 is 10), draw the problem and then write the corresponding equation (e.g. $16 - 6 = 10$). If students are ready, try a related problem such as 16 take away 8 to demonstrate the getting-to-a-10 strategy.

Student Book with teacher support

Students to complete: Guided Practice activities, p. 17, modelling with concrete materials as necessary.

OXFORD UNIVERSITY PRESS

Session 3: Topic introduction – Counting up to friendly numbers

WHOLE CLASS

Introductory activity: Friendly numbers

Write a subtraction problem on the board with numbers that are close together, e.g. 32 – 27. Invite students to estimate the answer. How could this help them know they have calculated the correct answer? Ask students to discuss with a partner how they would solve the problem. Provide an opportunity to share strategies. Model the counting-up strategy with 10-frames, highlighting why it can help to find the answer if you can count up to a 10 first. Involve students in modelling the strategy with similar problems, then try a problem where the numbers aren't close together, e.g. 42 – 18. Would counting up to a friendly number be the best strategy for this problem? What other strategies could students use?

AT-STANDARD AND EXTENSION GROUPS

Student Book

Students to complete: Guided and Independent Practice activities, pp. 19–20. Ask early finishers to get into pairs and roll two dice to make a 2-digit number and identify as quickly as possible how many more they need to count up to the nearest 10.

SUPPORT GROUP

Concept exploration and skill development: Friendly numbers and interactive number lines

Access an online interactive number line. Tell students they are going to subtract 19 from 24 by counting up to a friendly number. Ask students to start at 19 and then click on the next 10. Ask: "How many have been added so far? How many more still need to be added to get to the end number of 24? What do you think the difference between the two numbers will be?"

Now ask students to click on the end number. Ask: "How many do you need to count up to get from 19 to 24?" Write this as a difference between and subtraction problem, i.e. the difference between 19 and 24 is 5, so 24 – 19 is 5.

Repeat with other numbers.

Student Book with teacher support

Students to complete: Guided Practice activities, p. 19.

Session 4: Instruction and consolidation

WHOLE CLASS

Topic exploration: Which strategy?

List four subtraction problems on the board, such as 53 – 48, 36 – 8, 62 – 6 and 64 – 57. In pairs, ask students to discuss whether the getting-to-a-10 strategy or the counting-up-to-friendly-numbers strategy would be more effective for each one. Could either be used? Share some responses and the answers as a class.

AT-STANDARD GROUP

Teacher activity: Four in a row

Divide students into pairs and give them a number board and a set of number cards (from *BLM 4: Four in a row*), as well as two different coloured sets of counters. Students take turns to pick up two number cards and work out the difference between the numbers. If the answer is on the board, they put a counter of their colour on the number. If the number is already taken, the student draws two different number cards. Play continues until one student gets four of their counters in a row.

Student Book

Students to complete: Extended Practice activities, p. 21.

SUPPORT GROUP

Student Book with teacher support

Students to complete: Independent Practice activities, pp. 18 and 20, and Extended Practice activities, p. 21. As a group, check the answers to the Independent Practice activities, modelling any areas of difficulty using concrete materials, such as 10-frames or interlocking cubes. If students are ready, support them to complete the Extended Practice, modelling examples as appropriate.

EXTENSION GROUP

Student Book

Students to complete: Extended Practice activities, p. 21.

Activity sheet

Students to complete: *Activity sheet 4: Subtraction race*.

Practice and Mastery Book

See p. 3 for information about how to use the Practice and Mastery Book activities.

Session 5: Post-assessment

Students to complete: Post-test 3, Unit 1, Topic 4, p. 69.

Unit 1 Number and place value
Topic 5 Exploring subtraction

Student Book pages 22–27

Learning focus

Describe and choose written strategies for subtraction of 2-digit numbers

Materials

- sheets of paper, each with a number from 1–15
- 6-sided dice
- 10-frames
- coloured counters
- *BLM 2: Number lines 0–20*
- *Activity sheet 5: Eating chocolate*

Potential difficulties: Number fact recall

In order to be able to subtract quickly and successfully, students need to have recall of basic addition facts and corresponding subtraction facts.

- Regularly practise number bonds to 10 and then to 100, first with visual support, to build the bank of easily recalled facts that students have access to.
- Link addition and subtraction wherever possible so that students understand that one addition or subtraction fact links to three related facts.

Daily practice activity

On the first day, brainstorm all the words and symbols that students associate with subtraction. Draw on these to solve a simple subtraction problem each day, such as 15 – 9 = _____. Record the problem and answer in as many different ways as possible, e.g. using materials, on the interactive whiteboard, on a number line, as a horizontal number sentence.

Session 1: Pre-assessment
Students to complete: Pre-test 3, Unit 1, Topic 5, p. 68.

Session 2: Topic introduction – Subtracting on a number line

WHOLE CLASS

Introductory activity: Human number line
Choose 15 students to stand at the front of the class and give each one a piece of paper with a number from 1 to 15. Ask them to form a human "number line". Write a subtraction problem, such as 13 – 7, on the board and choose another student to model it on the number line, starting at 13 and counting back 7 to find the answer. Repeat with other problems, giving different students a turn.

AT-STANDARD GROUP

Student Book
Students to complete: Guided, Independent and Extended Practice activities, pp. 22–24. Ask early finishers to find, model and record different subtraction problems that result in a given target number, using different methods, such as an empty number line.

SUPPORT GROUP

Concept exploration and skill development: "Counting back" practice
Use *BLM 2: Number lines 0–20* to model counting back. As a class, start at the number 20. Then ask a student to roll a dice. Tell the whole class what number was rolled. Ask another student to count back that many on the number line, predicting first what number will be reached. Repeat with different students until you reach the number 0. Give each student their own copy of BLM 2 so they can then play the game on their own number lines.

Student Book with teacher support
Students to complete: Guided Practice activities, p. 22. Discuss with students which number to start from and why.

EXTENSION GROUP

Student Book
Students to complete: Guided, Independent and Extended Practice activities, pp. 22–24.

Activity sheet
Students to complete: *Activity sheet 5: Eating chocolate*.

OXFORD UNIVERSITY PRESS

Session 3: Topic introduction – Addition and subtraction are connected

WHOLE CLASS

Introductory activity: Human number line extended

Choose 15 students to stand at the front of the class and form a human number line, as in Session 2. Write an addition equation, such as 6 + 5 = _____, on the board and choose another student to model it on the number line, starting at 6 and counting up 5 to find the answer. Explain to students that knowing this can help them work out three other number facts. Model the following: 11 – 6 = 5, 11 – 5 = 6 and 5 + 6 = 11. Record the related facts. Repeat with other equations.

AT-STANDARD AND EXTENSION GROUPS

Student Book

Students to complete: Guided, Independent and Extended Practice activities, pp. 25–27. Ask early finishers to write five single addition or subtraction facts and swap them with a partner to complete the three related facts for each one.

SUPPORT GROUP

Student Book with teacher support

Students to complete: Guided and Independent Practice activities, pp. 25–26. Work through the Guided Practice activities together using 10-frames and coloured counters to model the problems. Support students to model the Independent Practice activities and complete them on their own.

Session 4: Instruction and consolidation

WHOLE CLASS

Topic exploration: Subtracting tens on a number line

Empty number lines are a useful tool to help students extend and record their thinking in subtraction. Write a simple equation, such as 36 – 13, on the board. Invite students to estimate the answer and discuss why this might be useful to do. Model for students how to represent the calculation on an empty number line using big jumps for the tens and little jumps for the ones. Was the final answer close to the estimate? Make a display of big jumps and little jumps by giving each student a 2-digit subtraction problem to solve on an empty number line. Model experimenting with colour coding the tens and ones, or using other prompts to help students remember how to correctly use the strategy.

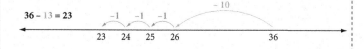

36 – 13 = 23

AT-STANDARD AND EXTENSION GROUPS

Teacher activity: Subtraction hangman

Play a group game of *Subtraction hangman*. Think of an equation, such as 26 – 11 = 15, but only reveal one part of it to students, e.g. _____ – 11 = _____. Give students a number range to work within and ask them to guess one of the missing numbers. Each incorrect guess earns a piece of the hangman. Once students have guessed one number correctly, they should be able to use their knowledge of addition and subtraction to find the second missing number. Students can then play the game themselves in pairs.

SUPPORT GROUP

Student Book with teacher support

Students to complete: Extended Practice activities, pp. 24 and 27. Ask students to form pairs and check each other's answers. Where there is disagreement, encourage students to talk through the strategy to try and agree on the correct response. While the students in the other groups are playing *Subtraction hangman*, discuss and model any difficulties this group is experiencing.

Practice and Mastery Book

See p. 3 for information about how to use the Practice and Mastery Book activities.

Session 5: Post-assessment

Students to complete: Post-test 3, Unit 1, Topic 5, p. 69.

Unit 1 Number and place value
Topic 6 Multiplying

Student Book pages 28–31

Learning focus

Use arrays and number lines to explore multiplication and repeated addition

Materials

- counters, small beanbags, hoops, 10-sided dice, coloured pencils, magazines (optional)
- *BLM 5: Array game board* (or a grid on an interactive whiteboard)
- *Activity sheet 6: Tim's Toyshop*

Potential difficulties: Interpreting multiplication

Some students may have difficulty differentiating between related multiplication facts, such as two groups of six and six groups of two.

- Give students plenty of hands-on practice with groups, encouraging them to tell how they have organised their groups to consolidate the concept.
- Use questioning to reinforce the underlying ideas: How many groups do you have? How many are in each group?

Daily practice activity

Identify equal groups of objects in the classroom, such as packets of pencils, arrangements of windows or pairs of shoes. Discuss quick ways of counting the items. Challenge students to find new things to count each day.

Session 1: Pre-Assessment

Students to complete: Pre-test 4, Unit 1, Topic 6, p. 70.

Session 2: Topic introduction

WHOLE CLASS

Introductory activity: Exploring "groups of"

Tell the class you are knitting winter booties for your dogs. You have three dogs and you want to know how many booties you will need. Divide students into mixed-ability pairs and ask them to draw a picture to help work out the answer, and then write

a sentence about the problem. Share responses as a class, listing the different ways that students chose to record their answers, e.g. in words, as repeated addition, as groups of. Discuss the "×" symbol as meaning "groups of". Repeat with other problems that allow students to easily represent groupings as part of their solutions.

AT-STANDARD GROUP

Student Book

Students to complete: Guided and Independent Practice activities, pp. 28–30. Ask early finishers to make and record different arrays using counters, and write the matching multiplication number sentence.

SUPPORT GROUP

Concept exploration and skill development: Skip counting for repeated addition

To practise skip counting to solve multiplication problems, give each student two small beanbags. Place three hoops on the floor and invite three students to put their beanbags in each one of the hoops so that there are two in each. Ask students to suggest how many beanbags there are in total. How do they know? Share strategies such as counting all and skip counting and discuss which is the fastest. Repeat with different numbers of hoops and beanbags, encouraging students to use "shortcuts" to find the answer as quickly as they can. Ask one student to count each beanbag individually while another skip counts so that students can clearly see how much more efficient repeated addition is.

Student Book with teacher support

Students to complete: Guided Practice activities, p. 28. Link students' knowledge of repeated addition with groups of.

EXTENSION GROUP

Student Book

Students to complete: Guided and Independent Practice activities, pp. 28–30.

Activity sheet

Students to complete: *Activity sheet 6: Tim's Toyshop*.

OXFORD UNIVERSITY PRESS

Session 3: Instruction and consolidation

WHOLE CLASS

Topic exploration: Understanding arrays

The concept of arrays can be a difficult one for students to understand. On a whiteboard, show students a simple 2×4 array and discuss its key features, including the fact that each column has the same number in it and each row has the same number, so there are no odd pieces. Do students know what a column and a row are? Choose 12 students and ask them to arrange themselves into an array with three columns and four rows. Repeat for other numbers, discussing how many students are in each row and how many are in each column. Extend students' thinking by making human arrays to explore different arrangements that represent the same total.

AT-STANDARD GROUP

Teacher activity: Experiencing arrays

Arrays are a useful tool to demonstrate the commutative property for multiplication. Enlarge *BLM 5: Array game board* (or use a grid on an interactive whiteboard). Ask a student to roll two 10-sided dice and then colour in an array on the game board based on the numbers rolled. For instance, if the student rolls 2 and 4, an array with 2 columns and 4 rows or 4 columns and 2 rows could be coloured. Then ask a second student to roll the dice and use a different colour to colour their array on the game board so that it doesn't overlap the first array. As play continues, there is less space on the board to place arrays, and students have to consider which combination of columns and rows is best. When no more moves can be made, the winner is the student with the most squares coloured in. Once students understand the game, allow them to play independently in pairs.

SUPPORT GROUP

Student Book with teacher support

Students to complete: Independent Practice activities, pp. 29–30. Check in with students as they work through the activities, discussing any difficulties and supporting them where needed.

EXTENSION GROUP

Student Book

Students to complete: Extended Practice activities, p. 31.

Multiplication fact practice

In pairs, give students *BLM 5: Array game board*, a 10-sided dice and coloured pencils. Tell them they will be practicing their two times tables. One student rolls the dice and colours an array that is "2 by" the number rolled, e.g. if a 3 is rolled, a 2 by 3 array is

coloured. The student also writes the multiplication fact inside the coloured array. Then the second student has a turn, again multiplying their number by 2 to get their array. Play continues until there is no more room on the game board and the winner is the student with the most squares coloured in. Students can practise other number facts in the same way, such as multiplying by 5 or by 3.

Session 4: Instruction and consolidation

WHOLE CLASS

Topic exploration: Repeated addition and multiplication

Invite five students to stand at the front of the class and hold up three fingers each. How many fingers are there altogether? Choose one student to write the equation as an addition number sentence, one student to write it as a multiplication number sentence and another student to give an oral explanation. Repeat with a different number of students and objects.

AT-STANDARD AND EXTENSION GROUPS

Student Book

At-standard students to complete: Extended Practice activities, p. 31. Ask early finishers and Extension students to model and draw as many different arrays as they can find using 24 counters.

SUPPORT GROUP

Concept exploration and skill development: Making groups

Ask students to draw four people. How many legs are there altogether? Support students to find the answer using skip counting and record it as repeated addition. Talk through how many groups of two legs there are and how many legs there are altogether. Then ask students to draw or find pictures of animals with four legs in magazines to show three groups of four. Support them to write it as repeated addition and, if appropriate, as a multiplication number sentence.

Student Book with teacher support

Students to complete in pairs: Extended Practice activities, p. 31.

Practice and Mastery Book

See p. 3 for information about how to use the Practice and Mastery Book activities.

Session 5: Post-assessment

Students to complete: Post-test 4, Unit 1, Topic 6, p. 71.

Unit 1 Number and place value
Topic 7 Dividing
Student Book pages 32–35

Learning focus

Explore division and repeated subtraction supported by visual cues

Materials

- interactive hundred chart
- counters
- paper plates
- large sheets of paper
- jelly beans (optional)
- dice
- *BLM 6: Party bag treats*
- *Activity sheet 7: Across the divide*

Activity sheet materials

- counters or other counting objects (optional)

Potential difficulties: Making equal groups

Some students may have difficulty creating equal groups, even when using concrete materials.

- Explicitly teach the skill of sharing out to each group one at a time in turn, reinforcing the concept with language such as, "One for you and one for me. One for you and one for me".
- Give students lots of real-life opportunities to practise equal sharing, e.g. when handing out materials for a lesson.

Daily practice activity

Pick a number of the day and explore which numbers can be equally divided by it, using an interactive hundred chart. Ask a student to pick a random number between 1 and 100. Then ask another student to use repeated subtraction to count back from the random number selected to see if they land on zero, which shows that the number can be exactly divided by the number of the day. Count how many times the number was subtracted to complete the division, e.g. 32 divided by 2 is 16.

Session 1: Pre-assessment

Students to complete: Pre-test 5, Unit 1, Topic 7, p. 72.

Session 2: Topic introduction

WHOLE CLASS

Introductory activity: Investigating equal groups

Tell students that you have a problem that you want them to solve. You have 15 carrot seeds and you want to plant them in three equal rows. How many should you plant in each row? Give students 15 counters and ask them to make a model to show how you should plant the seeds. Once they are happy with their arrangements, students can trace around their counters to record their solution. Discuss the responses, focusing on effective strategies for sharing, such as lining up the "seeds" in an array to clearly check that the same number is in each row. Write the division equation in words and as a number sentence using the division symbol.

AT-STANDARD GROUP

Student Book

Students to complete: Guided and Independent Practice activities, pp. 32–34. Ask early finishers to divide 16 carrot seeds into equal rows, and record their solutions.

SUPPORT GROUP

Concept exploration and skill development: Sharing

Give each student three paper plates and 12 counters. Ask them to share the counters equally between the plates. How many counters are on each plate? Model recording this as repeated subtraction and in words (12 divided by 3 = 4). Repeat the activity with other combinations, such as 12 counters and two plates, supporting students to share the counters equally and record their findings.

Student Book with teacher support

Students to complete: Guided Practice activities, p. 32. Use concrete materials to model the repeated subtraction process if required.

OXFORD UNIVERSITY PRESS

EXTENSION GROUP

Student Book

Students to complete: Guided and Independent Practice activities, pp. 32–34.

Activity sheet

Students to complete: *Activity sheet 7: Across the divide*.

Session 3: Instruction and consolidation

WHOLE CLASS

Topic exploration: Exploring equal groups

Experiment with dividing by different numbers by asking students to put themselves in equal groups. Start with counting how many students are in the class and then call out a number, such as 5. Students must organise themselves into groups of that number. How many groups could they make? Were there any students left over? Repeat with different numbers. Can students use their skip counting skills to predict if there are going to be any leftovers? Model recording successful combinations on the whiteboard using the division symbol.

AT-STANDARD GROUP

Teacher activity: Real-life division

It's important that students can relate division as equal shares to their everyday lives. Give each student *BLM 6: Party bag treats* and explain that they will be using the items to make up party bags for four people. On a large sheet of paper, ask students to draw the four people, cut out the party bag items and then share them among the party guests. Encourage students to write about what they did, in words or using number sentences. How many of each item would the guests receive?

SUPPORT GROUP

Student Book with teacher support

Students to complete: Independent Practice activities, pp. 33–34. Check in with students as they work through the activities, discussing any difficulties and supporting them where needed.

EXTENSION GROUP

Student Book

Students to complete: Extended Practice activities, p. 35.

Session 4: Instruction and consolidation

WHOLE CLASS

Topic exploration: Number line division

Number lines are another way to give visual reinforcement to the concept of division once students have had experience with physically sharing out items. On a whiteboard, make a number line from 0 to 20. Give context to the problem by telling students a story, e.g. "I have 20 cakes and I want to give two to each of my friends. How many friends can I give them to?" Model solving the problem on the number line by counting back in skips of two, verbalising the process as you go: "I have made one group and I have 18 cakes left to share". When you have finished, count the number of skips together to find the answer. Pose similar problems and invite the students to solve them using the number line.

AT-STANDARD AND EXTENSION GROUPS

Student Book

At-standard students to complete: Extended Practice activities, p. 35. Ask early finishers and Extension students to model their responses to Extended Practice, question 2, on a number line.

SUPPORT GROUP

Concept exploration and skill development: Exploring 16

Divide students into pairs and give them 16 counters (or jelly beans) and a dice. Ask one student to roll the dice and predict whether 16 can be evenly divided by the number rolled. Students then divide the 16 counters into that number of groups. Support students to record their findings as word or number sentences for successful shares, and to keep track of the numbers that 16 couldn't be evenly divided by.

Student Book

Students to complete: Extended Practice activities, p. 35.

Practice and Mastery Book

See p. 3 for information about how to use the Practice and Mastery Book activities.

Session 5: Post-assessment

Students to complete: Post-test 5, Unit 1, Topic 7, p. 73.

Unit 1 Number, pattern and function

Topic 8 Using addition and subtraction facts

Student Book pages 36–39

Learning focus

Develop strategies for memorising addition and subtraction number facts and use recall of number facts to solve problems

Materials

- counters
- calculators
- playing cards

Potential difficulties: Choosing the correct data display

Students who rely on counting to access number facts can sometimes have difficulty moving on to be able to reason or recall addition and subtraction facts.

- Provide opportunities for students to explore and identify patterns in number facts to build reasoning ability.
- Explicitly build students' understanding of fact families and of the relationships between addition and subtraction facts.

Daily practice activity

Explore adding a different number each day. For example, practise adding 2 to smaller numbers and then to larger numbers and encourage students to identify patterns, such as the fact that adding 2 to an odd number results in an odd number and adding 2 to an even number results in an even number.

Session 1: Pre-assessment

Students to complete: Pre-test 6, Unit 1, Topic 8, p. 74.

Session 2: Topic introduction

WHOLE CLASS

Introductory activity: Identifying addends

Write the number 9 on the board and invite students to suggest pairs of numbers that total 9. List their suggestions and verify as a class that they are correct. How can you be sure that you have found all the addend pairs to 9? Ask students to work with a partner to complete the same activity for the number 12. Share the results as a class, discussing strategies that allow for the addends to be found systematically. List the addends on the board in order (i.e. from 0 + 12 to 12 + 0), and ask students to describe any patterns they see. Allow students to apply their learning by finding the addend pairs for 15.

AT-STANDARD GROUP

Student Book

Students to complete: Guided and Independent Practice activities, pp. 36–38. Ask early finishers to work systematically to identify all the sets of three addends that total 9.

SUPPORT GROUP

Concept exploration and skill development: Linking addition and subtraction

As a group, find all the pairs of addends that total a target such as 8, using counters to model each one if students need visual support. Invite students to identify any combinations that use the same numbers, such as 3 + 5 and 5 + 3. Tell students that each of the pairs is part of a fact family for the target number, but there are two more members of the family in the form of subtraction facts. Ask students to suggest any subtraction facts that they could make using the same digits (e.g. 8, 5 and 3), prompting them that they should start with the largest number when making a subtraction fact if required. Record the two addition and related subtraction facts on the board and invite students to describe any patterns that they see.

In pairs, challenge students to find all the other members of the fact family for a new addition fact, such as 4 + 2 = 6, reminding them that there should be two addition and two subtraction facts. Model the fact family with counters as well as recording each of the four members on the board. Repeat for another fact family, this time starting with a subtraction fact, to consolidate students' understanding.

Student Book with teacher support

Students to complete: Guided Practice activities, p. 36.

Student Book

Students to complete: Guided and Independent Practice activities, pp. 36–38.

Session 3: Instruction and consolidation

WHOLE CLASS

Topic exploration: Subtraction strategies

Write a subtraction problem on the board, such as $17 - 9 = $ _____. Discuss the concept of estimating answers with students and ask them how they might go about estimating the answer to the problem and why they might do this. Next, ask students to think-pair-share about how they might work out the answer in their heads, discussing the strategies as a class. Lastly, give each pair a calculator and ask them to use it to solve the problem. Compare the three methods, asking students when you might use each.

Write five further subtraction problems on the board, starting with an easier one and including some at an appropriate level of challenge. In pairs, ask students to use all three methods in order – estimation, mental calculation and a calculator – to solve the problems. Bring students back together to share their solutions, and what their preferred strategies for particular problems were and why.

AT-STANDARD GROUP

Teacher activity: Practising fluency

Choose a target number such as 14 and record it on the board. Divide students into two teams and ask a representative from each team to draw five cards from a deck of playing cards. Explain that the Jack is worth 11, the Queen is worth 12 and the King is worth 13. Each team must use their cards to build addition combinations that total 14, using as few or as many addends as they like. A point is scored for each combination that the team finds. Once students understand the rules, allow them to play the game in pairs.

Bring students back together and demonstrate the same game but using subtraction. Choose a lower target, such as 3, and have students make subtraction equations using their cards that will result in 3 as the answer. For example, they might make $13 - 4 - 5 - 1$ or $7 - 4$. Ask students to play the game in pairs and share any hints they have for remembering addition and subtraction facts after playing it.

Student Book

Students to complete: Independent and Extended Practice activities, pp. 37–39.

SUPPORT GROUP

Student Book with teacher support

Students to complete: Independent and Extended Practice activities, pp. 37–39. Check in with students as they work through the Independent Practice activities, discussing any difficulties, before supporting them to complete the Extended Practice.

EXTENSION GROUP

Student Book

Students to complete: Independent and Extended Practice activities, pp. 37–39.

Practice and Mastery Book

See p. 3 for information about how to use the Practice and Mastery Book activities.

Session 4: Post-assessment

Students to complete: Post-test 6, Unit 1, Topic 8, p. 75.

Unit 2 Fractions and decimals
Topic 1 Fractions of objects
Student Book pages 40–43

Learning focus

Investigate and model numerical and visual representations of halves, quarters and eighths of whole objects and shapes in context

Materials

- paper shapes as wholes and cut into halves, quarters and eighths
- A4 paper
- paper plates (or paper circles of the same size)
- large sheets of paper
- scissors
- glue
- paper rectangles of three different sizes
- *Activity sheet 8: Computer patterns*

Potential difficulties: Ordering fractions

When ordering, students are used to identifying larger numbers. This can sometimes lead to confusion when they need to identify a larger fraction, given that the larger the denominator of a fraction is, the smaller the pieces are.

- Talk about the denominator as showing how many pieces an object has been divided into. Allow students to make physical comparisons of objects of the same size that have been divided into different fractions.
- It's useful to explicitly discuss the fact that the relationship between the denominator and the size of the fraction is different from counting integers.

Daily practice activity

Show a whole paper shape next to a half, quarter or eighth of the same shape. Ask students to identify what fraction the smaller piece is. Repeat each day with different shapes and fractions.

Session 1: Pre-assessment
Students to complete: Pre-test 7, Unit 2, Topic 1, p. 76.

Session 2: Topic introduction

WHOLE CLASS

Introductory activity: Representing equal shares

Ask students to draw how they would divide a pizza equally if they were sharing it with one other person. Then draw another pizza of the same size that is shared equally between four people and a third pizza shared equally between eight people. Discuss the results, focusing on the idea that the shares need to be equal. Talk about how many pieces make up halves, quarters and eighths, and have students label their pictures accordingly.

AT-STANDARD GROUP

Student Book

Students to complete: Guided and Independent Practice activities, pp. 40–42. Ask early finishers to practise folding an A4 piece of paper into halves, quarters and eighths.

SUPPORT GROUP

Concept exploration and skill development: Comparing fractions of the same object

Give each student two paper plates (or paper circles of the same size) and ask them to trace around the outside of each on a large sheet of paper. Tell students to cut the first plate in half, discussing strategies such as folding to make sure that the shares are equal. The second plate should be cut into quarters. Students should then glue one of their halves into the first circle outline, and one of the quarters into the second, labelling their pieces with words and symbols. Discuss the concept of the denominator determining the number of pieces in each fraction, e.g. a half is one piece out of two. If students are ready, give them a third paper plate and ask them how many pieces it should be cut into to make eighths. Follow the same process to explore what an eighth of the circle would look like.

Student Book with teacher support

Students to complete: Guided Practice activities, p. 40.

EXTENSION GROUP

Student Book

Students to complete: Guided and Independent Practice activities, pp. 40–42.

OXFORD UNIVERSITY PRESS

Activity sheet

Students to begin: *Activity sheet 8: Computer patterns.*

Session 3: Instruction and consolidation

WHOLE CLASS

Topic exploration: Comparing like-fractions

The idea that the physical size of a fraction of an object is determined by the size of the whole can be a difficult one to grasp. In pairs, provide students with paper rectangles of three different sizes. Ask students to divide each rectangle in half and paste them vertically onto a sheet of paper with the smallest halves at the top and the largest halves down the bottom. Repeat with three more rectangles but divide them into quarters. Ask students to share their observations. Are halves always the same size? Are quarters always the same size? Do they therefore think that eighths are always the same size? How could they check?

AT-STANDARD GROUP

Teacher activity: Writing fractions

Students need to be formally introduced to the conventions of writing fractions as symbols. Write $\frac{1}{2}$ on the board and ask students what it means. Can they draw what a half looks like? Do students know what the 1 and the 2 represent? To apply this knowledge, ask students to explain to a partner what $\frac{1}{4}$ means and what $\frac{1}{8}$ means. Discuss the connection between the word "quarter" and "four parts", making parallels with the prefix "quad" as meaning "four" to help students remember what a quarter is.

Student Book

Students to complete: Extended Practice activities, p. 43.

SUPPORT GROUP

Student Book with teacher support

Students to complete: Independent and Extended Practice activities, pp. 41–43. Check in with students as they work through the Independent Practice activities, discussing any difficulties, before supporting them to complete the Extended Practice.

EXTENSION GROUP

Student Book

Students to complete: Extended Practice activities, p. 43.

Activity sheet

Students to complete: *Activity sheet 8: Computer patterns.*

Practice and Mastery Book

See p. 3 for information about how to use the Practice and Mastery Book activities.

Session 4: Post-assessment

Students to complete: Post-test 7, Unit 2, Topic 1, p. 77.

Unit 2 Fractions and decimals
Topic 2 Fractions of groups
Student Book pages 44–47

Learning focus

Investigate and model numerical and visual representations of halves, quarters and eighths of collections

Materials

- packet of wrapped chocolates
- paper circles
- scissors
- counters
- *BLM 7: Pizza topping fractions*
- *BLM 8: Grouping children*
- *Activity sheet 9: Fraction mystery*

Potential difficulties: Interpreting fractions of groups

As students begin to understand that $\frac{1}{2}$ represents one part out of two, they can sometimes become confused when asked to find a fraction of a collection.

- Reinforce the idea that fractions represent part of a whole by giving students plenty of opportunities to manipulate groups of objects, and identify and label equal groupings.
- Ensure students understand that the numerator refers to the number of parts being discussed. Model the difference between one part of a whole divided into halves and one part of a group divided into halves.

Daily practice activity

Share a packet of chocolates with a student each day. Show the class how many you have altogether, e.g. 18 chocolates. Choose a student to share them with and give that student two, keeping the rest for yourself. As students react, discuss how the shares could be fair. If you both have an equal number, what fraction will that be? Repeat each day with different numbers, exploring dividing equally into halves, quarters and eighths.

Session 1: Pre-assessment

Students to complete: Pre-test 7, Unit 2, Topic 2, p. 76.

Session 2: Topic introduction

WHOLE CLASS

Introductory activity: Making equal collections

Give each student four paper circles to represent pizza bases and *BLM 7: Pizza topping fractions*. Tell students they need to cut out the toppings and put a quarter on each pizza. Share strategies for approaching the task. Discuss how many of each topping ended up on each pizza, checking that there is an equal number of each. Repeat with two paper circles for halves and eight paper circles for eighths. Ask students to share statements about their pizzas, e.g. "There were eight slices of tomato and I have two slices on each pizza. A quarter of eight is two".

AT-STANDARD GROUP

Student Book

Students to complete: Guided and Independent Practice activities, pp. 44–46. Ask early finishers to model and draw dividing a group of 24 into halves, quarters and eighths.

SUPPORT GROUP

Concept exploration and skill development: Fractions of 16

To practise dividing fractions into different groups, it can be useful to work with one number so students can compare the different fraction sizes. Give each student *BLM 8: Grouping children* and ask them to cut out the children and the fraction labels. Instruct students to divide the children in half and place a label under each group. How many children are there altogether? How many are in one half? Repeat with dividing the children into quarters and eighths. How many equal groups do students need to make for quarters? How many for eighths?

Student Book with teacher support

Students to complete: Guided Practice activities, p. 44.

EXTENSION GROUP

Student Book

Students to complete: Guided and Independent Practice activities, pp. 44–46.

Activity sheet

Students to begin: *Activity sheet 9: Fraction mystery*.

OXFORD UNIVERSITY PRESS

Session 3: Instruction and consolidation

WHOLE CLASS

Topic exploration: Different fractions of 16

To consolidate students' understanding of the relationship between a fraction and the size of a collection, it's useful to practise grouping collections in different ways. In pairs, give students *BLM 8: Grouping children* and ask them to cut out the children and fraction labels. Invite students to group the cut-outs in any way they like, e.g. they might make groups of children with hats and children without hats. Students should then match the appropriate fraction label to their groups. Share the different ways students chose to group the children and discuss which fractions the groupings represent and why. Allow students the opportunity to regroup their cut-outs into different fractional parts.

AT-STANDARD GROUP

Teacher activity: Understanding fractions as an equal part

Display 10 counters (or 10 items on an interactive whiteboard) but cover half of them with a piece of paper. Tell students they can see only half of the collection. How many counters must be under the paper? How many counters are in the collection altogether? Invite students to articulate their reasoning. Repeat with different numbers of counters. To challenge students, take a collection of 12 items and cover nine of them. Tell students they can see only a quarter of the collection. Can they work out how many counters are covered? Can they work out the total of the collection? Relate their responses to fractional concepts, e.g. "If I can see one quarter, then three quarters must be hidden, because there are four quarters altogether".

Student Book

Students to complete: Extended Practice activities, p. 47.

SUPPORT GROUP

Student Book with teacher support

Students to complete: Independent and Extended Practice activities, pp. 45–47. Check in with students as they work through the Independent Practice activities, discussing any difficulties, before supporting them to complete the Extended Practice.

EXTENSION GROUP

Student Book

Students to complete: Extended Practice activities, p. 47.

Activity sheet

Students to complete: *Activity sheet 9: Fraction mystery.*

Practice and Mastery Book

See p. 3 for information about how to use the Practice and Mastery Book activities.

Session 4: Post-assessment

Students to complete: Post-test 7, Unit 2, Topic 2, p. 77.

Unit 3 Money and financial mathematics
Topic 1 Notes and coins
Student Book pages 48–51

Learning focus

Use addition and multiplication to calculate whole number amounts using notes and coins

Materials

- a selection of coins
- 10 coins of the same value per student (or pair of students)
- 10-frames
- *BLM 9: 10-frames*
- *BLM 10: Hundred chart*
- *Activity sheet 10: International money*

Potential difficulties: Dollars and cents

In order to compare the value of notes and coins, students must have a solid grasp of the difference between dollars and cents. Without this, some students may believe that 50c is more than $20, for example, because 50 is bigger than 20.

- Stress the importance of identifying whether an amount of money is in dollars or cents in order to understand its value.
- Play simple comparison games to get students used to routinely thinking about relative values: Which is more: 5c or $5? Which is more: 20c or $5?

Daily practice activity

Each day, tell students that you have some coins in your pocket that equal a specific total, such as $1, and ask them to suggest which coins you may have.

Session 1: Pre-assessment
Students to complete: Pre-test 8, Unit 3, Topic 1, p. 78.

Session 2: Topic introduction
WHOLE CLASS
Introductory activity: Skip counting coins
Explain the concept of heads and tails to students. Then give each student 10 coins of the same value

and *BLM 9: 10-frames*. Before students flip the coins one coin at a time, ask them to guess whether it will land on heads or tails. If they guess correctly, they get to place the coin on their 10-frame and skip count to identify how much money they have. The winner is the first student to fill their 10-frame. Vary the game by playing with other coins.

AT-STANDARD GROUP
Student Book

Students to complete: Guided and Independent Practice activities, pp. 48–50. Ask early finishers to draw as many different ways to make $100 as they can.

SUPPORT GROUP
Concept exploration and skill development: Coins on a hundred chart

Enlarge a copy of *BLM 10: Hundred chart* so that it's big enough to place coins on. Lay out a pile of coins and choose a student to find the smallest denomination of coin from the pile, describing what they see on it once they find it. The student should then place the coin on the corresponding number on the chart – for example a 5c coin should be placed on the number 5. Repeat with other denominations of coins. For any coins of $1 or more, ask students where they would go on the chart and ensure they understand that $1 is 100c. Remove all the coins from the chart and ask students to collect all the smallest denomination coins you have. Work together to place them on the chart counting by that denomination. What is the total of your coins? How many coins are there? Repeat with the next smallest denomination.

Student Book with teacher support
Students to complete: Guided Practice activities, p. 48.

EXTENSION GROUP
Student Book
Students to complete: Guided and Independent Practice activities, pp. 48–50.

Activity sheet
Students to begin: *Activity sheet 10: International money.*

OXFORD UNIVERSITY PRESS

Session 3: Instruction and consolidation

WHOLE CLASS

Topic exploration: Money on an empty number line

Students should understand that the addition strategies they already know can be used to add amounts of money. Draw an empty number line on the whiteboard and ask students to suggest a way to make 25c using coins. List the coins and discuss the best order to add them in, and then represent the addition equation on an empty number line. Repeat the process for other combination suggestions, showing students that each of the successful combinations ends at the same point on the number line and is therefore equivalent. Students can work in pairs or individually to list and represent combinations of notes and coins that make a different total.

AT-STANDARD GROUP

Teacher activity: Charting equivalent values

Some students appreciate a structure for exploring different solutions to problems. Draw a coin combination chart on the whiteboard representing all the coins in your currency (see below for an example) and select a value to explore. It's easier to start with a smaller value, such as $1.30, while students get used to the format. Invite students to suggest different combinations of coins that could be used to make the designated value and record them in the chart. Encourage students to look for patterns and strategies to help them find combinations.

5c	10c	20c	50c	$1	$2	Total
	1	1		1		$1.30
2		1		1		$1.30
	1	1	2			$1.30

Practise with different values to consolidate the understanding that there are many different possibilities that are equivalent to one value.

Student Book

Students to complete: Extended Practice activities, p. 51.

SUPPORT GROUP

Student Book with teacher support

Students to complete: Independent and Extended Practice activities, pp. 49–51. Check in with students as they work through the Independent Practice activities, discussing any difficulties, before supporting them to complete the Extended Practice.

EXTENSION GROUP

Student Book

Students to complete: Extended Practice activities, p. 51.

Activity sheet

Students to complete: *Activity sheet 10: International money.*

Practice and Mastery Book

See p. 3 for information about how to use the Practice and Mastery Book activities.

Session 4: Post-assessment

Students to complete: Post-test 8, Unit 3, Topic 1, p. 79.

Unit 3 Money and financial mathematics
Topic 2 Counting money

Student Book pages 52–55

Learning focus

Count, calculate and problem-solve with coins

Materials

- a selection of coins and notes (real or play money)
- a large amount of coins of two different values
- supermarket catalogues
- scissors
- glue
- large sheets of paper
- coin dice
- *BLM 11: Coin tracks*
- *Activity sheet 11: Money transactions*

Potential difficulties: Money notation

Students will have varying levels of understanding of the ways to write different amounts of money.

- While some students may have experiences with and be ready for decimal notation ($1.50), it may be more appropriate for the majority of students to write totals of their counting in other ways, such as words (one dollar and fifty cents) or with the dollars and cents separated ($1, 50c).
- Be aware that some students may not fully understand decimal notation when they are looking at prices and may need extra support.

Daily practice activity

Each day, display different combinations of coins and notes on the whiteboard and ask students how much is in each collection, encouraging them to share counting strategies and regroup the coins to make them easier to count.

Session 1: Pre-assessment

Students to complete: Pre-test 8, Unit 3, Topic 2, p. 78.

Session 2: Topic introduction

WHOLE CLASS

Introductory activity: Finding equivalence

Give each student a small selection of coins, ensuring that some students have the same amount of money (but not the same selection of coins). Ask students to count how much money they have and find others in the class with the same amount. Once they've found their groups, ask students to make a chart showing the different combinations they have for the same value. Pair students who didn't find anyone with the same amount and ask them to decide which person has less money. These students should make a chart showing how much more is needed to make the two amounts equal.

AT-STANDARD GROUP

Student Book

Students to complete: Guided and Independent Practice activities, pp. 52–54. Ask early finishers to take a handful of coins and work with a partner to count and compare the amounts they have.

SUPPORT GROUP

Concept exploration and skill development: Coin tracks

Give each student *BLM 11: Coin tracks*, ten 5c coins and ten 10c coins. Ask them to put four 5c coins on the coin track. What is the last number they covered? Practise counting by fives to 20 to check that four 5c coins is the same as 20c. Ask students how many coins they will need to make 20c using 10c coins, and then check their answer by putting that number of coins on the coin track. Repeat with different numbers of coins, encouraging students to articulate how many coins they have used and to skip count to find the totals.

Student Book with teacher support

Students to complete: Guided Practice activities, p. 52.

EXTENSION GROUP

Student Book

Students to complete: Guided and Independent Practice activities, pp. 52–54.

Activity sheet

Students to begin: *Activity sheet 11: Money transactions*.

OXFORD UNIVERSITY PRESS

Session 3: Instruction and consolidation

WHOLE CLASS

Topic exploration: Exploring counting strategies

There are many different strategies that students can use to count small collections of coins and notes. Give each student some coins and notes, and a supermarket catalogue. Ask them to choose three things from the catalogue that they would like to buy, and then cut and paste them on a large sheet of paper. Using the money provided, get students to make the price of each item, drawing a representation of the price under the corresponding picture. Encourage students to group their notes and coins to make finding the total easier, and to draw their regrouped notes and coins under the original grouping. Invite students to share the methods they used, focusing on strategies such as skip counting to count coins or notes of the same value, and grouping dollars and cents separately.

AT-STANDARD GROUP

Teacher activity: Practising counting coins

As students become familiar with different denominations of coins, they will get faster at totalling them. To help with this, play a game of *Race to a dollar*. In pairs, give students a coin dice and a collection of coins. Students take turns to roll the dice and collect the corresponding coin. Each time, they should state how much money they now have in total and how much more they need to make $1. Play continues until one student rolls the coin value that will make exactly $1. The game can be varied to play up to $5 or by using notes instead of coins.

Student Book

Students to complete: Extended Practice activities, p. 55.

SUPPORT GROUP

Student Book with teacher support

Students to complete: Independent and Extended Practice activities, pp. 53–55. Check in with students as they work through the Independent Practice activities, discussing any difficulties, before supporting them to complete the Extended Practice.

EXTENSION GROUP

Student Book

Students to complete: Extended Practice activities, p. 55.

Activity sheet

Students to complete: *Activity sheet 11: Money transactions.*

Practice and Mastery Book

See p. 3 for information about how to use the Practice and Mastery Book activities.

Session 4: Post-assessment

Students to complete: Post-test 8, Unit 3, Topic 2, p. 79.

Unit 4 Patterns and algebra
Topic 1 Describing patterns
Student Book pages 56–59

Learning focus

Describe, extend and create number patterns

Materials

- class hundred chart (or *BLM 10: Hundred chart*)
- strips of paper
- blank pieces of paper
- small whiteboard and markers (optional)
- *BLM 12: Pattern table*
- *BLM 13: Missing digit strips*
- *Activity sheet 12: Finding patterns*

Potential difficulties: Counting fluency

Students who can't fluently skip count from a variety of starting points, or who don't have a good grasp of place value beyond two digits, may struggle with number pattern work.

- Support students with visual aids, such as number lines and hundred charts, and encourage them to verbalise each stage of the number sequence to help them identify pattern rules.
- If necessary, use object patterns to consolidate the concept of patterning without the extra complication of numbers for students who are less confident with counting skills.

Daily practice activity

Use a hundred chart to explore different number patterns to 100. Start a pattern and ask students to identify whether it's going backwards or forwards and what the rule is for the pattern.

Session 1: Pre-assessment
Students to complete: Pre-test 9, Unit 4, Topic 1, p. 80.

Session 2: Topic introduction
WHOLE CLASS
Introductory activity: Analysing patterns
Revise the concept of patterns with students and ask them to share examples of number, shape or other patterns they have seen or are familiar with. On the board, write a simple number pattern, such as 2, 4, 6, 8, 10, but make a mistake in it, explaining that there is an "alien" in your pattern. Ask students to identify the alien and what the number should really be. Repeat with a few more patterns until students get the idea. Give each student three strips of paper and ask them to create their own number pattern with an alien in it. Each pattern should have at least five correct numbers and only one alien. Students then swap their patterns with others in the class to see if they can identify the alien – they can even colour it green! Give students the opportunity to share some of their aliens, describing how they know which number doesn't belong.

AT-STANDARD GROUP
Student Book
Students to complete: Guided and Independent Practice activities, pp. 56–58. Ask early finishers to draw their own dot-to-dot picture using a number pattern.

SUPPORT GROUP
Concept exploration and skill development: Exploring number relationships
A table is a useful tool to help students see order in number patterns. Enlarge a copy of *BLM 12: Pattern table* (or draw it on an interactive whiteboard). Explain that you are going to look at how many hands there are in total in different groups of students. On the BLM, write the word *hands* in the blank space next to *Number of*. Start with one and ask how many hands one student has, noting this in the *Number of hands* column. Continue for two, three and four students, modelling the pattern by holding up hands. Can students predict how many hands five students will have? What about eight or 10? Complete the table and talk about the final digit patterns. Repeat to investigate different relationships, such as how many fingers students have or how many shoes they are wearing. Extend to other situations, such as "If one child has 10 pencils, how many will two children have?"

Student Book with teacher support

Students to complete: Guided Practice activities, p. 56.

EXTENSION GROUP

Student Book

Students to complete: Guided and Independent Practice activities, pp. 56–58.

Activity sheet

Students to begin: *Activity sheet 12: Finding patterns.*

Session 3: Instruction and consolidation

WHOLE CLASS

Topic exploration: Missing numbers

Students need to understand that the information they *do* have about a pattern is the key to finding missing numbers. Divide students into small groups and give each group one of the strips from *BLM 13: Missing digit strips*. As a group, students need to discuss and agree on what the missing numbers are. They shouldn't write on the strips themselves, but record the pattern number and their answer on a piece of paper or in their mathematics book. When they have finished one strip, groups can trade and try another. Share responses and strategies on completion. How did students go about finding the missing numbers? What information did they need?

AT-STANDARD GROUP

Teacher activity: Finding the rule

Students need lots of experience with analysing number patterns; those who aren't as able in this area often benefit from hearing how other students approached the problem. Write a number sequence (e.g. 1, 5, 9, 13) on the board and ask students to write the next number in the sequence on a piece of paper (or small whiteboard). Ask students to reveal their numbers, listing the different answers on the board. Write the correct number in the sequence. Now see if students can write the next number, again listing their answers. Did more students get it right? Choose someone with the correct answer and ask them to share their reasoning with the group. Can everyone get the next number in the sequence? Discuss what the rule for the pattern is and write it on the board. Try with different number patterns.

Student Book

Students to complete: Extended Practice activities, p. 59.

SUPPORT GROUP

Student Book with teacher support

Students to complete: Independent and Extended Practice activities, pp. 57–59. Check in with students as they work through the Independent Practice

activities, discussing any difficulties, before supporting them to complete the Extended Practice.

EXTENSION GROUP

Student Book

Students to complete: Extended Practice activities, p. 59.

Activity sheet

Students to complete: *Activity sheet 12: Finding patterns.*

Practice and Mastery Book

See p. 3 for information about how to use the Practice and Mastery Book activities.

Session 4: Post-assessment

Students to complete: Post-test 9, Unit 4, Topic 1, p. 81.

Unit 4 Patterns and algebra

Topic 2 Number sentences

Student Book pages 60–63

Learning focus

Represent and solve real-life addition and subtraction problems using number sentences

Materials

- coloured counters (or other manipulatives for counting)
- *BLM 14: Think board*
- *Activity sheet 13: Computer problem solving*

Potential difficulties: Symbolic representations

The jump from visual representations to number sentences can cause difficulties if students don't have a solid understanding of the underlying concepts.

- It can be useful to allow students to use drawings or concrete materials to support the introduction of number sentences so that the link is clear.
- Particular care must be taken with subtraction: if you remove objects when modelling problems, it can lead to confusion when students attempt to match the process to a number sentence but can no longer see all the elements. Strategies such as crossing out pictures, so that they can still be seen, can help make the operation clearer for students.

Daily practice activity

Invite students to write number sentences on the board to match everyday occurrences in the classroom. For example, if two students have green apples and three have red apples at snack time, write a number sentence to show how many students have apples altogether.

Session 1: Pre-assessment

Students to complete: Pre-test 9, Unit 4, Topic 2, p. 80.

Session 2: Topic introduction

WHOLE CLASS

Introductory activity: Linking mathematical representations

It's important that students understand that number problems can be represented in different ways. On the whiteboard, model a simple addition problem using two different colours of counters. Tell students that you are going to record the problem in two ways: in words and as a number sentence. Write a word problem to match your counters, e.g. "I have 7 red counters and 5 green counters. Altogether I have 12 counters". Then write the number sentence underneath: $7 + 5 = 12$. Discuss when each method might be appropriate and ensure students can see the connection between the counters, the word problem, and the number sentence. Repeat with different number combinations for both addition and subtraction, encouraging students to be creative in the word problems they suggest.

AT-STANDARD GROUP

Student Book

Students to complete: Guided and Independent Practice activities, pp. 60–62. Ask early finishers to write number sentences to match the word problems in question 3, p. 62.

SUPPORT GROUP

Concept exploration and skill development: Equality in number sentences

The idea of the equals sign as meaning "is equivalent to" is fundamental to students' ability to manipulate numbers and successfully write and solve number sentences. Write a simple number sentence on the board, such as $3 + 4 =$ _____, and ask students to solve it. Flip the sentence to read: _____ $= 3 + 4$. Are students able to immediately solve it? Model both sentences using manipulatives. Repeat with higher numbers until students grasp the concept.

Student Book with teacher support

Students to complete: Guided Practice activities, p. 60.

OXFORD UNIVERSITY PRESS

EXTENSION GROUP

Student Book

Students to complete: Guided and Independent Practice activities, pp. 60–62.

Activity sheet

Students to begin: *Activity sheet 13: Computer problem solving.*

Session 3: Instruction and consolidation

WHOLE CLASS

Topic exploration: Modelling number sentences

Organise students into small like-ability groups and give each group an addition or subtraction number sentence at their level of challenge. Ask them to invent a word problem to match their number sentence and present it to the class using drama, materials or any other method they find appropriate. After each presentation, discuss the key words used, such as "more", "total", "altogether" or "took away". Link each word to the addition or subtraction symbol in the original number sentence.

AT-STANDARD GROUP

Teacher activity: Using a think board

A "think board" can help to reinforce the relationship between number sentences and word problems, and offers extra scaffolding in the form of concrete and visual representations for students still working towards grasping the concept. Tell students a real-life problem, e.g. "There are 25 students in our class. Three are away today. How many students are here?" Give each student *BLM 14: Think board* and explain that they are going to show the problem in four different ways. Ensure that students have access to sufficient materials to model the problem and give them time to solve it. Challenge able students with a more difficult problem. Students can also use the think board to pose and solve problems of their own.

Student Book

Students to complete: Extended Practice activities, p. 63.

SUPPORT GROUP

Student Book with teacher support

Students to complete: Independent and Extended Practice activities, pp. 61–63. Check in with students as they work through the Independent Practice activities, discussing any difficulties, before supporting them to complete the Extended Practice.

EXTENSION GROUP

Student Book

Students to complete: Extended Practice activities, p. 63.

Activity sheet

Students to complete: *Activity sheet 13: Computer problem solving.*

Practice and Mastery Book

See p. 3 for information about how to use the Practice and Mastery Book activities.

Session 4: Post-assessment

Students to complete: Post-test 9, Unit 4, Topic 2, p. 81.

Unit 5 Using units of measurement

Topic 1 Length and area

Student Book pages 64–67

Learning focus

Estimate, measure and compare the length and area of familiar objects using uniform informal units

Materials

- grid paper
- uniform informal units for measuring length, such as craft sticks or paper clips
- uniform informal units for measuring area, such as square counters or sticky notes
- poster paper
- *Activity sheet 14: Bedroom decorating*

Activity sheet materials

- grid paper

Potential difficulties: Conservation of area

Some students may have difficulty understanding that the area of a set of shapes doesn't change even if they are rearranged and appear visually larger.

- Give students plenty of opportunities to compare the area of different shapes that are easy to measure, e.g. rectangles and squares, using informal units.
- Count the area of a set of different shapes made out of grid paper and record it in squares. Rearrange the shapes so that they are spread out and ask students to predict the area. Count the grid squares to confirm that the total hasn't changed.

Daily practice activity

Choose an object, such as the whiteboard, and ask students to show with their hands which part is the length and which is the area. Repeat with other objects each day to consolidate the concepts for students.

Session 1: Pre-assessment

Students to complete: Pre-test 10, Unit 5, Topic 1, p. 82.

Session 2: Topic introduction

WHOLE CLASS

Introductory activity: Comparing length and area

Divide students into mixed-ability pairs. Allocate one of the following to each pair: one flat item, such as a book or table top, and one long item, such as a pencil or the height of a bookshelf. Students must all use the same uniform informal unit to measure the area of their flat item and the length of their long item. Suitable units for length might be craft sticks or paper clips; suitable units for area might be square counters or sticky notes. Once pairs have measured their items, they should draw a diagram to show their results for length and area on a separate piece of paper. As a class, order the items to find the shortest and longest, and those with the greatest and smallest area, and make a display for the classroom.

AT-STANDARD GROUP

Student Book

Students to complete: Guided and Independent Practice activities, pp. 64–66. Ask early finishers to measure the items in Independent Practice activities, questions 1 and 4, with a different uniform informal unit, and compare the results.

SUPPORT GROUP

Concept exploration and skill development: Practising measuring length

Students need lots of practice measuring length with informal units to develop the skills needed for using formal units. Choose five different informal units of length, such as craft sticks, erasers, paper clips, whiteboard markers and matchsticks. In pairs, ask students to measure the length of a common item, such as their *Oxford Mathematics* book, with each of the materials and record their results. Discuss the findings as a group. Do students understand how to measure from end to end without leaving gaps? Do they notice that the larger the unit the fewer are needed? Did all students need more of the smaller units than the larger units for their measuring? Physically compare two items and check that the measurements recorded by the students accurately reflect the lengths of the items.

Student Book with teacher support

Students to complete: Guided Practice activities, p. 64, modelling measuring length and area without leaving gaps between each unit.

EXTENSION GROUP

Student Book

Students to complete: Guided and Independent Practice activities, pp. 64–66.

Activity sheet

Students to begin: *Activity sheet 14: Bedroom decorating.*

Session 3: Instruction and consolidation

WHOLE CLASS

Topic exploration: Measuring area

Students may already be familiar with the conventions used to measure length but may have less experience with area. On an interactive whiteboard, draw a small square prior to the lesson and duplicate it to make a number of rectangles that have an area that is easily measured, e.g. exactly three squares by two squares. Also draw a small circle that just fits into the original square. Ask students to estimate how many squares you will need to cover the first rectangle, allowing them to justify their responses. Invite one student to drag copies of the square to test their conjecture. Did the student align the edges of the square with the rectangle's edge? Were any of the squares overlapping? Compare the actual measurement with students' estimations. How accurate were they? Repeat with the circle, and ask students which shape was better to measure with. Are they aware that the circle leaves parts of the rectangle unmeasured?

AT-STANDARD GROUP

Teacher activity: Experimenting with area

To consolidate the concept of area as a flat surface, ask students to create their own shapes with the same area. On the whiteboard, demonstrate how four squares can be arranged in different configurations to make shapes all with an area of four squares.

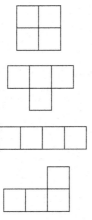

Give each student six square counters (or something similar) and ask them to make as many different shapes as they can with an area of six squares. Get students to trace or draw each shape onto poster paper and add a statement about their work underneath the shapes. Share the completed posters and discuss how students know the area of their shapes.

Student Book

Students to complete: Extended Practice activities, p. 67.

SUPPORT GROUP

Student Book with teacher support

Students to complete: Independent and Extended Practice activities, pp. 65–67. Check in with students as they work through the Independent Practice activities, discussing any difficulties, before supporting them to complete the Extended Practice.

EXTENSION GROUP

Student Book

Students to complete: Extended Practice activities, p. 67.

Activity sheet

Students to complete: *Activity sheet 14: Bedroom decorating.*

Practice and Mastery Book

See p. 3 for information about how to use the Practice and Mastery Book activities.

Session 4: Post-assessment

Students to complete: Post-test 10, Unit 5, Topic 1, p. 83.

Unit 5 Using units of measurement
Topic 2 Metres and centimetres

Student Book pages 68–72

Learning focus

Estimate, measure and compare lengths using standard units of mesurement

Materials

- 30 cm rulers
- meter rulers
- 10 cm strips of paper, plus other strips of paper of exact centimetre lengths
- uniform informal units for measuring length, such as craft sticks or paper clips
- A4 paper
- drinking straws
- long measuring tapes or trundle wheels
- *Activity sheet 15: Small dinosaurs*

Potential difficulties: Accurate measuring

If students don't have a solid understanding of the conventions of measuring length, they may find the leap to using formal units difficult.

- Ensure students have had plenty of practice with informal units and that they consistently align their measuring units with no gaps or overlaps.
- Practise measuring by moving a unit, e.g. using a single paper clip to measure the length of a small item. Ensure that students can accurately mark the end of the unit and then align it with that marking to further measure.

Daily practice activity

Each day, nominate an item in the room and ask students whether they would measure it in centimetres or metres, then have them estimate the length. Check as a class and monitor whether students' estimates improve through the week.

Session 1: Pre-assessment

Students to complete: Pre-test 10, Unit 5, Topic 2, p. 82.

Session 2: Topic introduction

WHOLE CLASS

Introductory activity: Using a ruler

Students need to be explicitly taught the conventions of accurate measurement with a ruler. Show students a 30 cm ruler and a metre ruler and discuss what they both are. Give each student (or pair of students) a 30 cm ruler and a 10 cm strip of paper. Ask students where they think they should put the paper to measure its length. Have all students find the zero on the ruler and align the paper with it. How long is the paper? Where on the ruler can students find this measurement? What unit is the ruler measuring in? Once a little more confident, give students paper strips of different lengths and ask them to measure them in centimetres and write the measurements down. Check that students are accurately measuring as they are working.

AT-STANDARD GROUP

Student Book

Students to complete: Guided and Independent Practice activities, pp. 68–71. Ask early finishers to estimate and check how many of an item, such as their pencil or pencil case, there will be in a metre.

SUPPORT GROUP

Concept exploration and skill development: Exploring rulers

It's important that students understand how rulers are constructed and what they are measuring. Give each student some paper clips and a piece of paper, and guide them to make their own paper clip ruler. Reinforce the fact that each of the markings should be the same distance apart, and show students how to number their ruler, starting from zero. Use the paper clip rulers to measure some smaller items in the class, such as the length of a pen. Do all the rulers give the same measurement for the same item? Why or why not?

Student Book with teacher support

Students to complete: Guided Practice activities, pp. 68 and 70. Assist students to measure accurately and to consider how to record part metres.

EXTENSION GROUP

Student Book

Students to complete: Guided and Independent Practice activities, pp. 68–71.

OXFORD UNIVERSITY PRESS

Activity sheet

Students to begin: *Activity sheet 15: Small dinosaurs.*

Session 3: Instruction and consolidation

WHOLE CLASS

Topic exploration: Using different measuring tools

It's good for students to have experience with using a variety of formal measuring tools. Show students how to make a paper plane from an A4 piece of paper, or provide a light object to throw that won't cause injury, e.g. a drinking straw. With their selected items, take students outside and get them to throw their items. Ask them to estimate and then measure the distance using a tape measure or trundle wheel, and record their results. Back inside, compare students' throws and ask students to suggest whether the estimate or the actual measurement for the distances was more important in this activity. Discuss the scales on the measuring tool used, e.g. a long tape measure has both metres and centimetres, and talk about how accurately the scale allowed students to measure the distances.

AT-STANDARD GROUP

Teacher activity: Measuring height

Measuring students' heights gives the opportunity to experience non-exact measurements. Ask one student to lie on the floor and another student to mark their head and feet with a marker such as a counter. Invite a third student to use a metre ruler to measure the student's height. Do they understand how to mark the end of the metre and start the next part of the measurement from zero on the scale? Once the measurement is complete, ask another student to check using a 30 cm ruler. How do the results differ? How are they the same? In pairs, allow students to measure and record each other's heights.

Student Book

Students to complete: Extended Practice activities, p. 72.

SUPPORT GROUP

Student Book with teacher support

Students to complete: Independent and Extended Practice activities, pp. 69 and 71–72. Check in with students as they work through the Independent Practice activities, discussing any difficulties, before supporting them to complete the Extended Practice.

EXTENSION GROUP

Student Book

Students to complete: Extended Practice activities, p. 72.

Activity sheet

Students to complete: *Activity sheet 15: Small dinosaurs.*

Practice and Mastery Book

See p. 3 for information about how to use the Practice and Mastery Book activities.

Session 4: Post-assessment

Students to complete: Post-test 10, Unit 5, Topic 2, p. 83.

Unit 5 Using units of measurement

Topic 3 Volume and capacity

Student Book pages 73–76

Learning focus

Estimate, measure and compare volume and capacity using uniform informal units. Understand the difference between volume and capacity

Materials

- interlocking cubes
- a variety of objects and different-sized containers to show volume and capacity
- a range of informal units for measuring volume, such as counters, tennis balls, blocks and pencils
- a piece of paper
- water or sand
- a range of informal units for measuring capacity, such as a tablespoon or plastic cup
- *Activity sheet 16: Make a container*

Activity sheet materials

- 12 blocks (or cubes)
- thin cardboard
- scissors
- glue or tape

Potential difficulties: Differentiating between volume and capacity

Even some adults have trouble explaining the difference between volume and capacity, so it's no surprise that the concepts can be confusing for students.

- Provide opportunities to compare the ideas, supporting learning with hands-on experience. Investigate ways to physically measure the capacity of a container and then its volume.
- Create a graphic organiser that shows words and experiences that relate to capacity (e.g. "holds more", "liquids" and "pouring") and words and experiences that relate to volume, (e.g. "takes up more space" and "solids").

Daily practice activity

Each day, present a different item and ask students to suggest how they could find its capacity or volume. Compare the items throughout the week and order in terms of volume or capacity.

Session 1: Pre-assessment

Students to complete: Pre-test 11, Unit 5, Topic 3, p. 84.

Session 2: Topic introduction

WHOLE CLASS

Introductory activity: Introducing volume

Give each student a handful of interlocking cubes and ask them to make a building using three cubes. Invite one student to share their response and record what their "building" looks like on the board – have any students made a different building? Share and discuss different ways that students made their buildings. Next, ask students to make as many different buildings as they can using five cubes. Once they have completed one, leave it in front of them while they make subsequent buildings to ensure they have created different ones. Share and record the results with the students, introducing the idea that the buildings all have the same volume: they all take up five cubes' worth of space.

AT-STANDARD GROUP

Student Book

Students to complete: Guided and Independent Practice activities, pp. 73–75. Ask early finishers to make each of the objects in Independent Practice, question 1, and order them from smallest to largest volume.

SUPPORT GROUP

Concept exploration and skill development: Measuring volume

Students can often take a little time to understand the need to completely fill a container with no gaps to account for its volume. In pairs, provide students with a small container such as a lunch box. Their challenge is to find the volume of the container. Make a range of measuring units available, such as interlocking cubes, counters, tennis balls, blocks and pencils, and ask students to record their findings. Share the results as a class, focusing on which units were good to measure volume and which were not so good. Were students able to measure the volume accurately enough to make comparisons with other groups?

Student Book with teacher support

Students to complete: Guided Practice activities, p. 73, using the language of volume and capacity to reinforce their understanding.

EXTENSION GROUP

Student Book

Students to complete: Guided and Independent Practice activities, pp. 73–75.

Activity sheet

Students to begin: *Activity sheet 16: Make a container.*

Session 3: Instruction and consolidation

WHOLE CLASS

Topic exploration: Comparing capacity

Before formal units of capacity are introduced, students need plenty of experience with estimating and measuring capacity using uniform informal units. This is important so students begin to build an understanding of comparing like with like. Provide the class with a wide variety of containers. In pairs or small groups, instruct them to choose five containers and order them from what they estimate to be the smallest capacity to the largest. Record their responses on a piece of paper. Using water or sand, ask students to check the capacity of each container with one uniform informal unit, such as a tablespoon or plastic cup, and record their answers. When the students have finished, discuss the differences between their estimates and the actual capacities. How did they find out which holds more? How can they be sure that their findings are correct? Discuss the importance to the end result of the units being uniform.

AT-STANDARD GROUP

Teacher activity: Estimating capacity

After students have had some experience with capacity, they should be able to compare the capacity of different containers by estimation. Divide the students into teams and send them on a "capacity treasure hunt". Write clues on the whiteboard and challenge each team to identify a container that matches the description. Examples of clues are: "Find a container that holds fewer than two teaspoons" and "Find a container that holds about the same amount as one coffee mug". Between five and ten clues works well. When the teams have recorded their items, discuss their responses as a group. For any disputed answers, allow students to measure the capacity of the container using the designated unit, in order to check if the estimate was accurate.

Student Book

Students to complete: Extended Practice activities, p. 76.

SUPPORT GROUP

Student Book with teacher support

Students to complete: Independent and Extended Practice activities, pp. 74–76. Check in with students as they work through the Independent Practice activities, discussing any difficulties, before supporting them to complete the Extended Practice.

EXTENSION GROUP

Student Book

Students to complete: Extended Practice activities, p. 76.

Activity sheet

Students to complete: *Activity sheet 16: Make a container.*

Practice and Mastery Book

See p. 3 for information about how to use the Practice and Mastery Book activities.

Session 4: Post-assessment

Students to complete: Post-test 11, Unit 5, Topic 3, p. 85.

Unit 5 Using units of measurement

Topic 4 Mass

Student Book pages 77–80

Learning focus

Estimate and compare the mass of familiar objects using balance scales

Materials

- pan balances
- uniform informal units, such as marbles, interlocking cubes or MAB materials
- larger objects for the pan balance, such as a tape dispenser, book or shoe
- *Activity sheet 17: Heaviest and lightest animals*

Potential difficulties: Weight and mass

Students are often incorrectly taught that weight is how heavy an object is in terms of the amount of matter it has. Although this is a common understanding, it's important that students know that *mass* is the correct mathematical term. Weight is actually a measure of the gravitational force on an object. As such, if we were to travel into space, our weight would change because the gravitational force would be different.

- Encourage students to think of situations involving the word "weight" and discuss whether "mass" is the more appropriate term.

Daily practice activity

At the beginning of the week, make a list of items in the classroom that are heavy and a list of those that are light. Encourage students to justify their classifications. Add to the lists throughout the week.

Session 1: Pre-assessment

Students to complete: Pre-test 12, Unit 5, Topic 4, p. 86.

Session 2: Topic introduction

WHOLE CLASS

Introductory activity: Using a pan balance

Students may not have been explicitly taught how to use a pan balance. Tell students that you are going to put a common item, such as a stapler, on one side of the balance and ask them to predict what will happen. Carry out the experiment. Now explain that you want to find out the mass of the stapler using a uniform informal unit, such as marbles. One by one, add marbles to the other side of the pan balance until the side with the stapler moves slightly. Ask students to explain what is happening. Add more marbles. Do students understand how to tell when the mass on each side of the balance is the same? What will happen to the stapler when the marbles become heavier? In mixed-ability pairs or small groups, ask students to estimate and then find the mass of their pencil case using uniform informal units. Allow them to experiment with making one side heavier than the other as well as finding the number of marbles that balances their item and have them try out their estimated number of units to see whether it is heavier or lighter than the object.

AT-STANDARD GROUP

Student Book

Students to complete: Guided and Independent Practice activities, pp. 77–79. Ask early finishers to find the mass of each of the items they used in Independent Practice, question 3, using the pan balance with uniform informal units.

SUPPORT GROUP

Concept exploration and skill development: Exploring mass

In small groups, give students a pan balance and access to a variety of objects to place on it, including multiples of smaller objects (e.g. marbles, interlocking cubes or MAB materials) and some larger single objects (e.g. a tape dispenser, book or shoe). Allow students time to experiment with the pan balance, then ask them to find items or groups of items that balance each other. Discuss the results of the students' investigations, focusing on the language of mass, such as "heavier" and "lighter".

Student Book with teacher support

Students to complete: Guided Practice activities, p. 77. Encourage them to verbalise the reasons for their answers.

EXTENSION GROUP

Student Book

Students to complete: Guided and Independent Practice activities, pp. 77–79.

OXFORD UNIVERSITY PRESS

Activity sheet

Students to begin: *Activity sheet 17: Heaviest and lightest animals.*

Session 3: Instruction and consolidation

WHOLE CLASS

Topic exploration: Comparing mass

Gather the pencil case masses recorded in the *Using a pan balance* activity. Ask for two volunteers who believe that their pencil case is particularly heavy to bring them forward. How do they know? Invite another student to heft both pencil cases. Which one feels heavier? Is this the same one that needed more marbles to balance it in the earlier activity? Repeat with different pencil cases and order them from lightest to heaviest. Allow students to heft the pencil cases in order to feel the difference.

AT-STANDARD GROUP

Teacher activity: Estimating mass

To consolidate the concept of mass, allow students to investigate and compare the mass of a variety of different things. Write a list of groups of uniform · informal units on the board, such as five marbles, 20 interlocking cubes and 40 paper clips. Students must choose an object in the room and estimate whether it has the same mass as the first group of units on the list. They should record their guess and then check to see how close they were using a pan balance. Repeat for other items. Did students' guesses improve? What strategies did students use to help them make good estimates? Encourage them to make comparative statements using their findings, such as "I thought the stapler would have the same mass as 10 marbles, but it was heavier".

Student Book

Students to complete: Extended Practice activities, p. 80.

SUPPORT GROUP

Student Book with teacher support

Students to complete: Independent and Extended Practice activities, pp. 78–80. Check in with students as they work through the Independent Practice activities, discussing any difficulties, before supporting them to complete the Extended Practice.

EXTENSION GROUP

Student Book

Students to complete: Extended Practice activities, p. 80.

Activity sheet

Students to complete: *Activity sheet 17: Heaviest and lightest animals.*

Practice and Mastery Book

See p. 3 for information about how to use the Practice and Mastery Book activities.

Session 4: Post-assessment

Students to complete: Post-test 12, Unit 5, Topic 4, p. 87.

Unit 5 Using units of measurement

Topic 5 Time

Student Book pages 81–84

Learning focus

Read and write digital and analogue time to the hour, half hour and quarter hour

Materials

- a clock (real or teaching clock)
- scissors
- split pins
- *BLM 15: Clock face and hands*
- *Activity sheet 18: A day out*

Potential difficulties: Hour hand position

Some students may get confused by the hour hand when trying to read "quarter past" and "quarter to" times.

- Where possible, use a real clock to demonstrate the movement of the hands, allowing students to see the progression of the hour hand from one number to the next as the minute hand moves around.
- Explicitly teach the idea that the "past" times relate to the number that the hour hand has just passed, while the "to" times relate to the number the hour hand is coming to. Give students plenty of opportunities to read and model different times.

Daily practice activity

Choose five students, or five pairs of students, to be time watchers each day. Allocate each student or pair a time during the day representing hours, quarter hours and half hours. As each time arrives, the student (or students) allocated to that time should draw a clock face showing the time and create an accompanying picture that represents what the class is doing. Students with times over recess or lunch breaks will have to take note of what they are doing and complete their task when the break is over. Order the times and display them around the classroom.

Session 1: Pre-assessment

Students to complete: Pre-test 13, Unit 5, Topic 5, p. 88.

Session 2: Topic introduction

WHOLE CLASS

Introductory activity: Making a clock face

Photocopy *BLM 15: Clock face and hands* onto card and give one to each student. Ask them to cut out the pieces and make a clock with moving hands using split pins. Seat students in a circle and call out a time, such as 9 o'clock. Students have 10 seconds to make the time on their clock faces, after which they must reveal their clocks. Those with the correct time get to stay in and continue with the game. Discuss the placement of the minute and hour hands for different times so that all students understand representing time to the quarter hour.

AT-STANDARD GROUP

Student Book

Students to complete: Guided and Independent Practice activities, pp. 81–83. Ask early finishers to get into pairs and use their clocks (from the *Making a clock face* activity) to make a time for their partner to write in digital and analogue format.

SUPPORT GROUP

Concept exploration and skill development: Time and fractions

To help students understand and remember times to the quarter hour, it can be useful to relate the clock face to fractional parts. Divide a circle into halves longways on the whiteboard and ask students what each part is called. Repeat with quarters. Draw or insert a clock face on the board that is about the same size as the circles. Invite students to compare the right half of the circle with the clock face, focusing on identifying the number at the top and the bottom of the half. Link this to the position of the minute hand for half past times. Ask students to use their clocks (from the *Making a clock face* activity) to model the hour hand moving halfway around the clock, and the minute hand moving halfway between two numbers.

Compare the top-right quarter of your circle with the clock face. What do students notice? Can they relate this to the positioning of the minute hand for

OXFORD UNIVERSITY PRESS

quarter past times? Show students what the clock face would look like with three quarters of the circle placed on it, starting from the 12. Which two numbers can they still see on the clock? Relate this to where the minute hand is when it's three quarters of the way around the clock. What time does this represent? Have students practise making quarter past and quarter to times, verbalising where the minute hand is, e.g. "It's quarter past 2, so the minute hand is one quarter of the way around the clock, pointing at the number 3".

Student Book with teacher support

Students to complete: Guided Practice activities, p. 81, using their clocks to model times if required.

EXTENSION GROUP

Student Book

Students to complete: Guided and Independent Practice activities, pp. 81–83.

Activity sheet

Students to begin: *Activity sheet 18: A day out*.

Session 3: Instruction and consolidation

WHOLE CLASS

Topic exploration: Clock hands

Ask students to imagine they are clocks. Call out a time category, such as "o'clock" or "quarter to". Invite students to use one arm to show where the big hand would be. Take care to ensure that students don't mirror a clock that is facing them so that they understand the placement of the hand in relation to them as a clock face. The activity can be played in two ways: as a class, where those who are incorrect are eliminated, or, to extend students, in pairs, where students make times for each other to guess using their arms as the hands of the clock.

AT-STANDARD GROUP

Teacher activity: Conceptualising time to the quarter hour

Play a game of *Who am I?* with time as the subject. Give students clues such as: "My big hand is on the 12. My small hand is on the one. What time is it?" Invite students to suggest or write down the answer. You could also play the game in teams and see which team gets the most correct answers. Vary the clues to include times to the quarter hour, and give reverse clues such as: "The time is quarter past 3. Where is the big hand?" If necessary, start by giving students a clock face to make the times suggested by the clues before moving to a more abstract interpretation of times.

Student Book

Students to complete: Extended Practice activities, p. 84.

SUPPORT GROUP

Student Book with teacher support

Students to complete: Independent and Extended Practice activities, pp. 82–84. Check in with students as they work through the Independent Practice activities, discussing any difficulties, before supporting them to complete the Extended Practice.

EXTENSION GROUP

Student Book

Students to complete: Extended Practice activities, p. 84.

Activity sheet

Students to complete: *Activity sheet 18: A day out*.

Practice and Mastery Book

See p. 3 for information about how to use the Practice and Mastery Book activities.

Session 4: Post-assessment

Students to complete: Post-test 13, Unit 5, Topic 5, p. 89.

Unit 5 Using units of measurement
Topic 6 Measuring time

Student Book pages 85–88

Learning focus

Estimate and compare lengths of time using universal units of measure

Materials

- stopwatches
- sticky notes
- three large sheets of paper
- online stopwatch
- analogue clock with minute increments

Potential difficulties: Calculating conversions

Students who do not have sound reasoning and calculation skills may struggle to convert between units of time.

- Focus on the operations and process used to convert between units by allowing students to use calculators to make the conversions.
- List and practise number facts that are directly related to time conversions, such as knowing multiples of 60.

Daily practice activity

Invite students to estimate the duration of a different classroom activity each day. Measure and record the actual duration and allow students to compare this with their estimates and to evaluate whether they chose an appropriate unit of time for their estimate.

Session 1: Pre-assessment

Students to complete: Pre-test 14, Unit 5, Topic 6, p. 90.

Session 2: Topic introduction

WHOLE CLASS

Introductory activity: Exploring minutes and seconds

Give pairs of students a stopwatch and make sure that they understand how to use it. Ask students to time each other writing the alphabet backwards and ask them to record the time in minutes and seconds. Have each student write their time on a small card and then invite students to arrange themselves from shortest to longest time. Back in their pairs, have students convert their times to seconds and then ask the class to again organise themselves from shortest to longest time. Did the order change? Why or why not?

AT-STANDARD GROUP

Student Book

Students to complete: Guided and Independent Practice activities, pp. 85–87. Ask early finishers to list all the units of time referred to in the Guided and Independent activities and order them from shortest to longest.

SUPPORT GROUP

Concept exploration and skill development: Comparing duration

To give students a sense of the relative duration of seconds and minutes, use an online stopwatch. Start the stopwatch and clap to keep time with the changing of the seconds. Invite students to think of ways that they could count in seconds without a stopwatch; for example by inserting a common word or phrase between numbers such as 'cat and dog'. Allow students to try their own counts while you time 10 seconds to see how accurate they can be.

As a group, watch the stopwatch run up to one minute, encouraging students to keep their own count in their heads. At what number did the seconds count change to minutes? Why? Discuss with students what the next biggest unit of time after minutes is and how many minutes they would need to wait until the stopwatch changes to an hour.

Student Book with teacher support

Students to complete: Guided Practice activities, p. 85.

EXTENSION GROUP

Student Book

Students to complete: Guided and Independent Practice activities, pp. 85–87.

OXFORD UNIVERSITY PRESS

Session 3: Instruction and consolidation

WHOLE CLASS

Topic exploration: Different units of time

With students, brainstorm activities they will partake in throughout the day, such as brushing their teeth, walking to school and sleeping. Ask each student to choose five activities and record how long they think each one takes them. Put students into groups of four and ask them to discuss the times they allocated to each activity to see if they think these are reasonable. Give each student five sticky notes and ask them to record one of their chosen activities on each. Write the heading *Seconds* on one large piece of paper, *Minutes* on another piece of paper and *Hours* on a third piece of paper, and invite students to place their sticky notes on the correct one. As a class, review the results to see if there is any disagreement about the duration of particular activities and discuss the reasons why this might be the case.

AT-STANDARD GROUP

Teacher activity: Representing time relationships

Show students an analogue clock with minute increments between the hours. Discuss what the increments represent and invite students to suggest how many there are and why. Talk to students about the fact that the clock is a tool that shows the relationship between minutes and hours. List with students the different units of time that they are aware of. In pairs, challenge students to design their own tool or diagram that shows how at least two of the units are related to each other. Give students the opportunity to present their work to the rest of the group or to the whole class.

Student Book

Students to complete: Extended Practice activities, p. 88.

SUPPORT GROUP

Student Book with teacher support

Students to complete: Independent and Extended Practice activities, pp. 86–88. Check in with students as they work through the Independent Practice activities, discussing any difficulties, before supporting them to complete the Extended Practice.

EXTENSION GROUP

Student Book

Students to complete: Extended Practice activities, p. 88.

Practice and Mastery Book

See p. 3 for information about how to use the Practice and Mastery Book activities.

Session 4: Post-assessment

Students to complete: Post-test 14, Unit 5, Topic 6, p. 91.

Unit 5 Using units of measurement

Topic 7 Months and seasons

Student Book pages 89–92

Learning focus

Understand the months and characteristics of seasons

Materials

- poster paper
- *BLM 16: Months and seasons cards*
- *Activity sheet 19: What season is it?*

Activity sheet materials

- an atlas (or the internet)

Potential difficulties: Writing and recognising months and seasons

The spelling of some months and seasons is quite tricky, which can make it difficult for students to recognise and correctly write them.

- Encourage students to share tips for remembering how to spell more challenging words, e.g. "Think of February the way it's written, rather than the way we would normally say it".
- Offer any tips of your own, such as linking the word "autumn" with the adjective "autumnal" to help students remember the "n" on the end.

Daily practice activity

Practise the order of the months of the year by chanting them each day, inviting students to stand up when the month they were born in is called out. Use references to the seasons throughout the day, e.g. "Those of you born in summer can return to your desks first" or "Those of you born in winter can get your lunches first". Begin to challenge students as their confidence grows, e.g. "Go and start your work if you were born in a month after July".

Session 1: Pre-assessment

Students to complete: Pre-test 13, Unit 5, Topic 7, p. 88.

Session 2: Topic introduction

WHOLE CLASS

Introductory activity: Season characteristics

It's helpful for students to understand how the months are grouped into seasons. Make four large "Y charts", one for each season, and record what each season looks like, sounds like and feels like to the students.

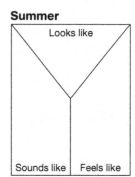

Discuss and record common characteristics of the months in each season, such as weather, activities and clothing. Extend students' thinking by introducing other cultural interpretations of seasons, such as the Indigenous seasons in the south of Australia.

AT-STANDARD GROUP

Student Book

Students to complete: Guided and Independent Practice activities, pp. 89–91. Ask early finishers to choose their favourite month and write five things they like about it, and what season it's in.

SUPPORT GROUP

Concept exploration and skill development: Exploring months and seasons

Individually or in pairs, allocate a month or season to students, then brainstorm as a group the significant events or attributes associated with that month or season. Ask students to write their month or season at the top of a sheet of poster paper and draw associated activities or objects. Give students time to share their interpretations with the whole class at the end of the lesson. Create a display of the posters, ordering the months into each season. You can also add each student's birthday to the posters and discuss which season each child was born in.

OXFORD UNIVERSITY PRESS

Student Book with teacher support

Students to complete: Guided Practice activities, p. 89, focusing on the correct order of the months and seasons.

EXTENSION GROUP

Student Book

Students to complete: Guided and Independent Practice activities, pp. 89–91.

Activity sheet

Students to begin: *Activity sheet 19: What season is it?*

Session 3: Instruction and consolidation

WHOLE CLASS

Topic exploration: Ordering months and seasons

Hand out the cards from *BLM 16: Months and seasons cards*, to a group of students. You can also allocate jobs such as timer and order judge to other students. Ask those with the month cards to get in order as quickly as possible; those with the season cards need to stand in front of the group of months they relate to. Time how long this takes students to complete. Repeat by giving the cards to different students and see if they can improve the times.

AT-STANDARD GROUP

Teacher activity: Recognising months and seasons words

To give students practice at recognising the words for the seasons and months of the year, play a game of *Concentration*. In pairs, give students two cut-out sets of cards from *BLM 16: Months and seasons cards*. Ask them to lay out the cards face-down in a four by eight array. One at a time, ask students to turn over two cards. If the cards match, the student gets to keep them; if they don't, the cards are turned back over. The winner is the student with the most cards at the end of the game. You can vary the game by asking students to find the months and seasons in order.

Student Book

Students to complete: Extended Practice activities, p. 92.

SUPPORT GROUP

Student Book with teacher support

Students to complete: Independent and Extended Practice activities, pp. 90–92. Check in with students as they work through the Independent Practice activities, discussing any difficulties, before supporting them to complete the Extended Practice.

EXTENSION GROUP

Student Book

Students to complete: Extended Practice activities, p. 92.

Activity sheet

Students to complete: *Activity sheet 19: What season is it?*

Practice and Mastery Book

See p. 3 for information about how to use the Practice and Mastery Book activities.

Session 4: Post-assessment

Students to complete: Post-test 13, Unit 5, Topic 7, p. 89.

Unit 5 Using units of measurement
Topic 8 Calendars
Student Book pages 93–96

Learning focus

Read and interpret calendars to determine the date and explore similarities and differences between months

Materials

- calendar page of the current month
- calendar for the current year, to be displayed along a wall
- *BLM 17: Calendar template*
- *Activity sheet 20: Day-of-year calendars*

Potential difficulties: Months that start late in the week

Some students can be confused by calendar representations when a month starts late in the week and, therefore, the last few days of the month prior appear in the first row of the calendar *before* the first day of the next month.

- Use different representations of calendars on the internet and any examples that you have in the classroom to show and explain this to students.
- Ask prompt questions, e.g. "What date is the first Sunday of the month?", to help students conceptualise that while the 30th or 31st might appear at the top of the calendar, those dates are actually the last days of the previous month.

Daily practice activity

Display a calendar of the current month and fill in key events that will happen, such as school excursions or term breaks. Each day, invite a student to identify the date and where it's on the calendar. Ask questions that relate other events to the day, e.g. "How many days until our excursion?" or "How many days have passed since Ben's birthday?"

Session 1: Pre-assessment
Students to complete: Pre-test 15, Unit 5, Topic 8, p. 92.

Session 2: Topic introduction

WHOLE CLASS

Introductory activity: Constructing a calendar

Help students understand how calendars are used to organise time. Use *BLM 17: Calendar template* to make a calendar for the next month. Begin by asking students to record the month at the top. Then instruct students to write the days of the week in the first row of boxes and fill in the dates. You may need to model where to start on an enlarged copy of the template, ensuring students understand that "1" represents the first day of the month, not necessarily the first box in the table. Once complete, ask students to draw a picture that represents the month in the large box. Discuss significant dates for the class and give students the opportunity to fill these in. Allow students to add to the calendar as new events arise during the month.

AT-STANDARD GROUP

Student Book

Students to complete: Guided and Independent Practice activities, pp. 93–95. Ask early finishers to write questions about their calendar (from the *Constructing a calendar* activity) and give them to a partner to answer.

SUPPORT GROUP

Concept exploration and skill development: Characteristics of the months

To help consolidate students' understanding of the order and number of days in each month, play a game of *Who am I?* Give students clues, e.g. "I come sometime after July. My name has eight letters in it. I have 30 days. Who am I?" Initially, scaffold students by displaying a calendar with the months clearly visible and allow them to give reasons for their answers. As students become familiar with the game, remove some displays. Do students remember the order of the months? Do they know how many days are in each month? Share strategies for remembering.

Student Book with teacher support

Students to complete: Guided Practice activities, p. 93. Encourage students to point to the correct days before writing their answers.

OXFORD UNIVERSITY PRESS

EXTENSION GROUP

Student Book

Students to complete: Guided and Independent Practice activities, pp. 93–95.

Activity sheet

Students to begin: *Activity sheet 20: Day-of-year calendars.*

Session 3: Instruction and consolidation

WHOLE CLASS

Topic exploration: Identifying important dates

Being able to see a calendar and relate it to known events is a good strategy to help familiarise students with how calendars work. Display the 12 months of the year on a calendar horizontally along a wall and ask each student to find their birthday and write their name on that day. As a class, record a few statements about the display, for example, "Merlin, Ishaan and Ava all have their birthdays on the 16th of a month" or "Cam's birthday is one week before Malaya's". Once students understand the concept, send them off to write five statements about their own birthday, relating it to other days and dates on the calendar. Allow students to share their statements in small groups and check whether they are correct. You can also record their birthdays on an interactive whiteboard calendar to keep.

AT-STANDARD GROUP

Teacher activity: Using the language of calendars

In pairs, students will play a game similar to *Battleship* using a copy of a calendar for the current month. First, ask students to record four special events on their calendars, such as music lessons, sports practice, birthdays or public holidays, without their partner seeing. Then students take turns to guess where the events are on the calendar, using appropriate language such as, "Is there an event on the third Tuesday of the month?" The winner is the first to locate all for four events. You may like to model the game with students guessing your events first.

An alternative is to set up a game board on an interactive whiteboard and have two teams of students race to find the hidden events.

Student Book

Students to complete: Extended Practice activities, p. 96.

SUPPORT GROUP

Student Book with teacher support

Students to complete: Independent and Extended Practice activities, pp. 94–96. Check in with students as they work through the Independent Practice activities, discussing any difficulties, before supporting them to complete the Extended Practice.

EXTENSION GROUP

Student Book

Students to complete: Extended Practice activities, p. 96.

Activity sheet

Students to complete: *Activity sheet 20: Day-of-year calendars.*

Practice and Mastery Book

See p. 3 for information about how to use the Practice and Mastery Book activities.

Session 4: Post-assessment

Students to complete: Post-test 15, Unit 5, Topic 8, p. 93.

Unit 6 Shape

Topic 1 2D shapes

Student Book pages 97–100

Learning focus

Identify and represent 2D shapes according to their characteristics

Materials

- digital camera
- shape blocks
- feely bag
- *Activity sheet 21: Shape patterns*

Potential difficulties: Irregular shapes

If students are only exposed to regular shapes, they may have difficulty recognising and classifying irregular shapes or making generalisations about shapes.

- Ensure a mixture of representations of each type of shape is included when you are exploring shape attributes. For example, when discussing triangles, show students a variety to help them develop the concept that any three-sided shape is a triangle.
- Support students to list the attributes of a specific shape. Then offer them both regular and irregular examples, as well as some that aren't that particular shape at all, to sort and classify.

Daily practice activity

Focus on a different shape each day. Use a variety of mathematical terms to describe the shape, including whether or not it has parallel sides and whether it has straight or curved sides. Ask students to find and bring in examples of shapes they discover in their everyday lives. Put the shapes on display for everyone in the class to see.

Session 1: Pre-assessment

Students to complete: Pre-test 16, Unit 6, Topic 1, p. 94.

Session 2: Topic introduction

WHOLE CLASS

Introductory activity: Identifying shapes in the environment

Ask each student to find a shape in the room. Examples include: the rectangle of the door or the tabletop, the square of the window or the circle of the top of the bin. Take a photo of each shape with a digital camera and print them out. Hand out the images to the students and discuss what each shape is. Where appropriate, explain to students the connection between the shapes and their names – for example, the prefix 'quad' means four and therefore quadrilaterals have four sides. Ask students to write a description of their shape, including the name of the shape and its key features, and to draw the outline of the shape. Make a class display of the photos and descriptions as a visual reference for students.

AT-STANDARD GROUP

Student Book

Students to complete: Guided and Independent Practice activities, pp. 97–99. Ask early finishers to draw a picture using at least five different shapes, making sure that each shape is labelled.

SUPPORT GROUP

Concept exploration and skill development: Identifying shapes

Put a collection of shapes into a feely bag. Allow students to feel, describe and name them, focusing on properties such as corners and sides. Challenge students to find a particular shape by name, such as a square, or by description, such as a four-sided shape. Discuss the similarities and differences between shapes, e.g. a trapezium and a square both have four straight sides and four corners. How are they different?

Student Book with teacher support

Students to complete: Guided Practice activities, p. 97, making connections between the shapes they have become familiar with from the Introductory activity and those on the page.

EXTENSION GROUP

Student Book

Students to complete: Guided and Independent Practice activities, p. 97–99.

OXFORD UNIVERSITY PRESS

Activity sheet

Students to begin: *Activity sheet 21: Shape patterns.*

Session 3: Instruction and consolidation

WHOLE CLASS

Topic exploration: Exploring shapes with digital technologies

Many computer and interactive whiteboard programs have built-in tools that allow for easy creation of shapes. On an interactive whiteboard, model creating shapes using a tool such as **Auto Shapes** in Word. Invite students to come up and make specific shapes, such as circles, rectangles, rhombuses and diamonds, and then ask them to suggest ways to group these shapes. When students are confident with using the tools, challenge them to use **Auto Shapes** to copy pictures that you make on the board, such as a rocket.

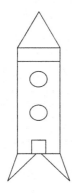

Discuss the shapes used and the attributes of these shapes.

WHOLE CLASS

Topic exploration: 2D shapes in 3D shapes

Show students a real-life 3D shape such as a tissue box. Invite them to suggest which 2D shapes they can see on each of the faces. How many times is each 2D shape repeated to make the 3D shape? Give small groups of students a different real-life object to examine and ask them to record the shapes of the faces and how many of each shape there are. Swap the 3D shapes around to allow students to work with two or three different options. Come together as a class and compare students' findings. Which 2D shapes were commonly used to create the 3D shapes?

AT-STANDARD GROUP

Teacher activity: Classifying shapes

Students need lots of opportunities to analyse the attributes of shapes. Draw four different shapes in colour on the whiteboard, e.g. a square, a trapezium, an irregular triangle and an oval. Ask students to nominate the odd one out and explain their reasoning. Encourage students to think of multiple solutions, focusing on geometric language that includes "corners", "sides" and "line types". Repeat

with different combinations of shapes. Challenge students to create their own groups of shapes, either by drawing shapes or selecting them from a set of shape blocks, and swap them with a partner to find the shape that doesn't belong in the group. Share the responses with the class.

Student Book

Students to complete: Extended Practice activities, p. 100.

SUPPORT GROUP

Student Book with teacher support

Students to complete: Independent and Extended Practice activities, pp. 98–100. Check in with students as they work through the Independent Practice activities, discussing any difficulties, before supporting them to complete the Extended Practice.

EXTENSION GROUP

Student Book

Students to complete: Extended Practice activities, p. 100.

Activity sheet

Students to complete: *Activity sheet 21: Shape patterns.*

Practice and Mastery Book

See p. 3 for information about how to use the Practice and Mastery Book activities.

Session 4: Post-assessment

Students to complete: Post-test 16, Unit 6, Topic 1, p. 95.

Unit 6 Shape

Topic 2 3D shapes

Student Book pages 101–104

Learning focus

Sort, describe and label 3D shapes according to their characteristics

Materials

- 3D solids
- sheets of paper
- pencils (to trace)
- scissors
- poster paper
- glue (optional)
- hoops
- examples of everyday 3D shapes
- *Activity sheet 22: Which object is that?*

Potential difficulties: Identifying properties

Some students may have difficulty recognising the features of objects.

- Provide 3D solids and have students look at one property at a time, e.g. the number of edges. Allow students to feel and count the corners, edges etc.
- Make a chart of the objects and their properties that students can refer to.

Daily practice activity

Focus on a different 3D shape each day. Use a variety of mathematical terms to describe the shape to reinforce concepts such as faces and edges. Ask students to find and bring in examples of 3D shapes they discover in their everyday lives. Ask students to classify the objects before putting them on display in the classroom.

Session 1: Pre-assessment

Students to complete: Pre-test 17, Unit 6, Topic 2, p. 96.

Session 2: Topic introduction

WHOLE CLASS

Introductory activity: Linking 2D shapes and 3D shapes

Show students a solid cube and ask them to look at the faces. What shape can they see? Take a piece of paper and put it over one of the faces. Fold the paper around the edges, trace the square that is revealed and then cut out the square. Show students how the square fits onto all six of the faces.

Divide students into mixed-ability pairs and give them a 3D shape and poster paper. Ask them to explore the shapes of the faces using the process modelled, and make a poster showing their original object and what they found out about it. They can also glue their cut-out faces on the poster.

AT-STANDARD GROUP

Student Book

Students to complete: Guided and Independent Practice activities, pp. 101–103. Ask early finishers to identify the shapes that make each 3D shape in Independent Practice, question 3, and try to draw each of them.

SUPPORT GROUP

Concept exploration and skill development: Sorting and classifying objects

Exploring different ways to sort and classify objects can help students to remember the attributes of different objects. Set out some hoops and provide a range of 3D shapes, both solids and everyday items. Invite students to examine the objects and group them using hoops, verbalising their reasoning for placing objects in particular groups. Overlapping the hoops allows students to classify 3D shapes using different and shared features, similar to a Venn diagram. Encourage students to explore the language of geometry, grouping by features such as edges, corners and faces, and support them to physically count the attributes if necessary. Make a group of 3D shapes and see if students can identify the criterion used to classify them.

Student Book with teacher support

Students to complete: Guided Practice activities, p. 101, making connections between the 3D shapes you have been working with and those on the page.

OXFORD UNIVERSITY PRESS

EXTENSION GROUP

Student Book

Students to complete: Guided and Independent Practice activities, pp. 101–103.

Activity sheet

Students to begin: *Activity sheet 22: Which object is that?*

Session 3: Instruction and consolidation

WHOLE CLASS

Topic exploration: Representing objects

On an interactive whiteboard, model drawing 3D shapes using a tool such as **Auto Shapes** in Word. Make a cube, cylinder or rectangular prism and ask students to create their own representations of each object on a computer. Encourage them to experiment with different orientations and representations of each shape before allowing them to print out the results. Students can paste their work onto poster paper and label each object.

AT-STANDARD GROUP

Teacher activity: Identifying object features

Students need opportunities to practise applying their knowledge of 3D shapes in different situations. Creating an object train is one activity that helps students to identify the features of solids. Provide the group with 3D shape models and everyday objects. Ask one student to select an object. Then ask a second student to select a different object that has one feature in common with the first object. Place the 3D shapes side by side. Ask the second student to name the 3D shape chosen and articulate the attribute that the two items have in common. For example, if the first object is a cube, the second might be a square pyramid because both objects have a square-shaped face. Continue the process until as many objects as possible have been chosen.

Student Book

Students to complete: Extended Practice activities, p. 104.

SUPPORT GROUP

Student Book with teacher support

Students to complete: Independent and Extended Practice activities, pp. 102–104. Check in with students as they work through the Independent Practice activities, discussing any difficulties, before supporting them to complete the Extended Practice.

EXTENSION GROUP

Student Book

Students to complete: Extended Practice activities, p. 104.

Activity sheet

Students to complete: *Activity sheet 22: Which object is that?*

Practice and Mastery Book

See p. 3 for information about how to use the Practice and Mastery Book activities.

Session 4: Post-assessment

Students to complete: Post-test 17, Unit 6, Topic 2, p. 97.

Unit 7 Location and transformation
Topic 1 Interpreting maps

Student Book pages 105–108

Learning focus

Describe and interpret the position of objects and places on maps in everyday contexts

Materials

- examples of different maps, e.g. street directories, travel maps, tourist guides
- small and large pieces of paper
- scissors
- *Activity sheet 23: Treasure Island*

Potential difficulties: Changing perspectives

Students following directions or describing the relative position of features on a map can become confused about the point that the directions are coming from.

- Give students opportunities to physically locate themselves on a grid, or in a room for which they have a floor plan, to help them conceptualise the relationship between the way they are facing and the interpretation of the directions.
- Discuss how directions can change depending on which way you are facing. For example, if a student is facing the front of the room, the window might be on their left, but if they are facing the back of the room, it's on their right.

Daily practice activity

Each time you leave the room as a class, choose a different student to describe the route you will take, using the language of direction. You could also draw the route on a map of the school, for example, using an enlarged copy of the evacuation map, and discuss the different regions and boundaries within the school.

Session 1: Pre-assessment

Students to complete: Pre-test 18, Unit 7, Topic 1, p. 98.

Session 2: Topic introduction

WHOLE CLASS

Introductory activity: Exploring maps

Provide students with a variety of different maps, such as street directories, travel maps and tourist guides. In small mixed-ability groups, give students time to explore the maps and make a list of their discoveries. Write some guiding questions on the board. For example: What do we use maps for? Where do you see maps? What do you find on maps? Allow students to share their findings at the end of the session.

AT-STANDARD GROUP

Student Book

Students to complete: Guided and Independent Practice activities, pp. 105–107. Ask early finishers to write a set of directions to get from one place to another using the map on p. 107. Then have them swap the directions with a friend to see if they work.

SUPPORT GROUP

Concept exploration and skill development: Directional language

It's very important that students can fluently use the language of direction, such as "left", "right", "next to" and "above" if they are to successfully interpret and use maps. Allow students to practise these terms by giving them simple placement instructions that they can physically follow. For example, say: "Pria should stand on the left side of Darcy". Watch students as they interpret the directions. To add a fun element, incorporate *Simon says* into the activity, where students are out if you don't say "Simon says" before giving the directions.

Student Book with teacher support

Students to complete: Guided Practice activities, p. 105, making connections between the language used in the activities and the instructions that they physically carried out.

EXTENSION GROUP

Student Book

Students to complete: Guided and Independent Practice activities, pp. 105–107.

Activity sheet

Students to begin: *Activity sheet 23: Treasure Island*.

OXFORD UNIVERSITY PRESS

Session 3: Instruction and consolidation

WHOLE CLASS

Topic exploration: Writing directions

Mapping is quite an abstract concept for many students; activities that allow them to relate maps to a familiar physical location can help bridge the gap between the abstract and the concrete. Take students outside and ask them to create a simple map of the playground, incorporating school or area boundaries. Students should then write directions from one place to another on their maps. Once complete, ask them to swap their maps with a friend and see if they were able to follow the directions to successfully arrive at the correct destination. Afterwards, discuss which aspects of the students' directions worked well and which aspects created any problems.

AT-STANDARD GROUP

Teacher activity: Mapping the classroom

Being able to compare and analyse different representations of the same place is a powerful way for students to learn about representing places on maps and interpreting what they see. In pairs, ask students to identify the important key features of the classroom that should be included on a map. Get them to think about how these key features could be represented before drawing each one on paper and cutting them out. Provide large pieces of paper for students to use as the classroom outline and instruct students to glue their features in the correct places. Compare the finished maps, discussing the size and position of various objects. How accurate are the maps? Do they have all the important features? Can students interpret each other's maps? You could also create a master map on an interactive whiteboard, discussing the relative position of each item.

Student Book

Students to complete: Extended Practice activities, p. 108.

SUPPORT GROUP

Student Book with teacher support

Students to complete: Independent and Extended Practice activities, pp. 106–108. Check in with students as they work through the Independent Practice activities, discussing any difficulties, before supporting them to complete the Extended Practice.

EXTENSION GROUP

Student Book

Students to complete: Extended Practice activities, p. 108.

Activity sheet

Students to complete: *Activity sheet 23: Treasure Island*.

Practice and Mastery Book

See p. 3 for information about how to use the Practice and Mastery Book activities.

Session 4: Post-assessment

Students to complete: Post-test 18, Unit 7, Topic 1, p. 99.

Unit 7 Location and transformation

Topic 2 Slides and flips

Student Book pages 109–112

Learning focus

Investigate, describe and represent the effects of translation and reflection transformations on shapes

Materials

- paint
- paint brushes
- paper
- *BLM 18: Alphabet template*
- *Activity sheet 24: Sliding around*

Activity sheet materials

- grid paper

Potential difficulties: Visualisation

Some students may have difficulty recognising a shape as the same as another if it has been flipped.

- Give students plenty of practice tracing around shapes, flipping them and tracing them again, guiding them to fit the shape back into both outlines to observe that the shape is the same, even though it looks different.
- Use geometric language to prompt students' thinking when comparing shapes that have been flipped. For example: How many corners has the first shape got? What about the second? Do both shapes have straight sides?

Daily practice activity

Spend five minutes each day playing common board games such as *Snakes and ladders*, *Tiddlywinks* or *Othello* on the interactive whiteboard to get students used to the terms "slide" and "flip". Encourage students to vocalise the movements of their game pieces using the language of transformation.

Session 1: Pre-assessment

Students to complete: Pre-test 19, Unit 7, Topic 2, p. 100.

Session 2: Topic introduction

WHOLE CLASS

Introductory activity: Experimenting with flips

Create "butterfly paintings" in class with students. Ask students to make a design in paint on one side of the page, then fold the paper and press down lightly on it. When the paper is re-opened, a flipped image of the original design appears on the blank side of the page. Display the finished artwork around the room to remind students what flipped shapes look like.

AT-STANDARD GROUP

Student Book

Students to complete: Guided and Independent Practice activities, pp. 109–111. Ask early finishers to write their names in capital letters and experiment to see which of the letters look the same when they are flipped.

SUPPORT GROUP

Concept exploration and skill development: Conceptualising slides and flips

Allowing students to experience first-hand the concepts of sliding and flipping is a good way to help them understand the terms, and appeals to kinaesthetic learners. Brainstorm what students know about the word "slide". Where have they seen things that slide? What happens to them? Invite students to demonstrate a slide with their bodies. Talk about what has changed and what has stayed the same. Are they still facing the same way? Repeat the process with flips, discussing where students have heard the word and inviting demonstrations.

Once students are familiar with both concepts, ask them to spread out in order to play a game. Call out "slide" or "flip" and instruct students to use their bodies to move the correct way.

Student Book with teacher support

Students to complete: Guided Practice activities, p. 109, making connections between the examples in the book and students' knowledge of moving in the same way.

OXFORD UNIVERSITY PRESS

EXTENSION GROUP

Student Book

Students to complete: Guided and Independent Practice activities, pp. 109–111.

Activity sheet

Students to begin: *Activity sheet 24: Sliding around.*

Session 3: Instruction and consolidation

WHOLE CLASS

Topic exploration: Investigating the effect of slides and flips

Digital technologies offer an effective way for students to make comparisons between shapes that have been transformed by sliding and flipping. Draw a shape, such as a trapezium, on an interactive whiteboard. Make a copy of the shape and fit it over the first one. Invite a student to slide the second shape to a new position. Discuss the direction in which the shape was moved – was it vertical, horizontal or diagonal? Compare the second shape with the first shape. Can students identify what has changed and what is the same? Repeat with other shapes.

Align the second shape back on top of the first one and use the flip command to flip the shape vertically. Move the shape below the first one in order for students to compare the two. Repeat with a horizontal flip. What do students notice? Experiment with other shapes to see which ones look the same and which look different after horizontal and vertical flips. Students could also try the activity themselves using digital technology, sharing their findings as a class.

AT-STANDARD GROUP

Teacher activity: Observing slides and flips

Copy *BLM 18: Alphabet template* onto card and give one to each student. Ask them to cut out the letters of their name and trace them along the top of a piece of paper. Once students are finished, ask them to repeat the activity, this time sliding the letters into a new position. Next, instruct them to create a flipped version of their name. In order to do this, suggest aligning the letters back on top of the original tracing and flipping each letter vertically downward. Allow students to share some of their creations, discussing the transformations in each version. Students can decorate the three versions of their name for classroom display.

Student Book

Students to complete: Extended Practice activities, p. 112.

SUPPORT GROUP

Student Book with teacher support

Students to complete: Independent and Extended Practice activities, pp. 110–112. Check in with students as they work through the Independent Practice activities, discussing any difficulties, before supporting them to complete the Extended Practice.

EXTENSION GROUP

Student Book

Students to complete: Extended Practice activities, p. 112.

Activity sheet

Students to complete: *Activity sheet 24: Sliding around.*

Practice and Mastery Book

See p. 3 for information about how to use the Practice and Mastery Book activities.

Session 4: Post-assessment

Students to complete: Post-test 19, Unit 7, Topic 2, p. 101.

Unit 7 Location and transformation

Topic 3 Half turns and quarter turns

Student Book pages 113–116

Learning focus

Investigate, describe and represent the effect of the rotation transformation for half and quarter turns

Materials

- scissors
- large pieces of paper
- clock face with movable hands
- grid paper (optional)
- *BLM 19: Shape templates*
- *Activity sheet 25: Amazing turns*

Potential difficulties: Visualising turns

Some students may have difficulty visualising the outcome of a half or quarter turn on a shape.

- Throughout activities on the topic, encourage students to make and justify predictions about the effects of the turns.
- Allow students plenty of hands-on practice with the concepts. Soft toys can be helpful to make turns with, as the change in their orientation is much more apparent than for many geometric shapes.

Daily practice activity

Introduce students to popular dances that involve half or quarter turns, e.g. the "Nutbush". Discuss the size and direction of the turn as students learn and practise the dances.

Session 1: Pre-assessment

Students to complete: Pre-test 19, Unit 7, Topic 3, p. 100.

Session 2: Topic introduction

WHOLE CLASS

Introductory activity: Turning shapes

Using a whiteboard, demonstrate to students how marking a dot on a shape can help track half and quarter turns. Then give each student *BLM 19: Shape templates* and ask them to cut out the shapes. Encourage them to explore which shapes look different when a quarter and half turn has been executed and which shapes look the same. Give students a large piece of paper, ask them to trace their shapes and record their findings under each shape. Encourage them to make statements about the effect of quarter and half turns on each shape. Share the results as a class.

AT-STANDARD GROUP

Student Book

Students to complete: Guided and Independent Practice activities, pp. 113–115. Ask early finishers to work with a partner to predict and test what everyday objects, such as pencils or rulers, will look like with half and quarter turns applied.

SUPPORT GROUP

Concept exploration and skill development: Making half and quarter turns

Students will be familiar with the terms "half" and "quarter" in reference to fractions of an object or collection, but may not have come across them in the context of geometry. Show students a clock face with the minute hand pointing to the 12. Ask them to identify where the hand will point to when it has travelled halfway around the clock. Repeat for quarter turns, starting from 12, 3 and 6. Ask students to stand up and make a half turn as if they were the minute hand of the clock. Which way are they facing now? See if students can make a quarter turn from that point. Use reference points in the class to help them identify how far to turn. You can also practise half and quarter turns outside on a clock face marked out in chalk to give students a clear idea of the magnitude of each turn.

Student Book with teacher support

Students to complete: Guided Practice activities, p. 113, ensuring they test their answers by making the same turns with their bodies.

EXTENSION GROUP

Student Book

Students to complete: Guided and Independent Practice activities, pp. 113–115.

Activity sheet

Students to begin: *Activity sheet 25: Amazing turns.*

OXFORD UNIVERSITY PRESS

Session 3: Instruction and consolidation

WHOLE CLASS

Topic exploration: Investigating the effect of half turns and quarter turns

Digital technologies are a useful tool to demonstrate the effect of turns on a shape. Draw a shape on an interactive whiteboard or similar. Choose a shape that looks different at each quarter turn around a fixed point, such as an L-shape. Make a copy of the shape and fit it over the first one. Use the rotate tool to turn the second shape 90° to the right. Discuss the effect of the turn, comparing the second shape with the first one. Can students identify what has changed and what is the same? Continue rotating by 90° until the shape is back over the original, each time discussing the effects of the turn.

AT-STANDARD GROUP

Teacher activity: Turns in real-life situations

To show students the relevance of understanding half and quarter turns, draw a grid on the board with a path marked from one object to another.

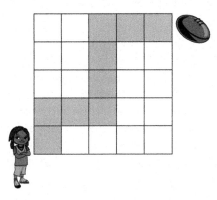

Ask students to describe the path taken in terms of steps forwards and turns taken. Some students may need to act out the movements to help them conceptualise whether the quarter turns are to the right or left at each point in the journey. When students have reached the end of the path, ask them what sort of turn they would need to make to turn back. Students could then create and describe their own paths on grid paper.

Student Book

Students to complete: Extended Practice activities, p. 116.

SUPPORT GROUP

Student Book with teacher support

Students to complete: Independent and Extended Practice activities, pp. 114–116. Check in with students as they work through the Independent Practice activities, discussing any difficulties, before supporting them to complete the Extended Practice.

EXTENSION GROUP

Student Book

Students to complete: Extended Practice activities, p. 116.

Activity sheet

Students to complete: *Activity sheet 25: Amazing turns.*

Practice and Mastery Book

See p. 3 for information about how to use the Practice and Mastery Book activities.

Session 4: Post-assessment

Students to complete: Post-test 19, Unit 7, Topic 3, p. 101.

Unit 8 Data representation and interpretation
Topic 1 Collecting data

Student Book pages 117–120

Learning focus

Explore and apply data collection and recording methods

Materials

- attribute blocks
- *Activity sheet 26: Popular names*

Potential difficulties: Asking the right questions

Some students may have difficulty with generating questions to gather data; it's important that these students have the opportunity to discuss possible variables that they could investigate.

- Incorporate questioning explicitly into different areas of the curriculum and encourage students to talk about the kinds of answers that particular questions generate.
- In addition, providing question prompts that are visible in the classroom will support students who are having difficulty developing their own questions.

Daily practice activity

Use oral language activities, such as *Show and tell* to develop questioning techniques in students. Encourage students to consider questions with yes/no answers, as well as those that require richer responses.

Session 1: Pre-assessment
Students to complete: Pre-test 20, Unit 8, Topic 1, p. 102.

Session 2: Topic introduction

WHOLE CLASS

Introductory activity: Investigating questions

Suggest a general topic to the class, such as school holidays, and ask each student to write one question about the topic. Discuss the questions generated. Which questions have only yes/no answers? Sort the questions into categories and choose one that

might be suitable for collecting data, discussing why it's suitable. Using the question selected, conduct a quick survey and record the results on the board. Were the results what students expected? Was it a good question to ask?

AT-STANDARD GROUP

Student Book

Students to complete: Guided and Independent Practice activities, pp. 117–119. Ask early finishers to write five questions about the dinner data on p. 117, and then swap them with a partner to answer.

SUPPORT GROUP

Concept exploration and skill development: Sorting data

It can be helpful for some students to physically see the data they are working with before progressing to recording data in a written form. Place a large handful of attribute blocks in front of students and ask them to suggest a way to sort them, e.g. by colour or shape. Sort the blocks together and create a simple table to record the data using ticks. Count the totals for each category. Then sort the blocks in a different way. Call on students to help you complete a table to record the new data. Each time, ensure that there are the same number of ticks as there are shapes to help students check their work.

Student Book with teacher support

Students to complete: Guided Practice activities, pp. 117–118, ensuring they check that they have the same number of ticks as names.

EXTENSION GROUP

Student Book

Students to complete: Guided and Independent Practice activities, pp. 117–119.

Activity sheet

Students to begin: *Activity sheet 26: Popular names*.

Session 3: Instruction and consolidation

WHOLE CLASS

Topic exploration: Collecting data

In identifying suitable questions, it's important for students to be aware that they will need to select a topic or concept where the variable is one category, e.g. favourite fruit or after-school activities. Use a prompt question with only two different choices as the answer. For example, "What's your favourite pet – a cat or a dog?" Ask 10–12 students to answer the question by standing on a particular side of the room according to their response. Record their names on a display under the appropriate categories. Brainstorm other questions with one categorical variable that students could ask in order to support them in understanding how to gather information suitable for data displays and analysis.

AT-STANDARD GROUP

Teacher activity: Formulating questions

To consolidate the concept of asking closed questions to gather information for data displays, play a game of *20 questions*. Choose an object in the room but don't tell the students what it is. Then prompt them to ask 20 questions to try to find out what object you have chosen. You can respond with only "yes" or "no". Students will quickly learn that they can't ask open questions, such as "Where is it?", or "or questions", such as "Is it in this half of the room or that half of the room?" Once the game has ended, discuss with students which questions were the most effective, highlighting the language that was used. Play again, possibly with a student as the object selector, and see if students become faster at winning the game.

Student Book

Students to complete: Extended Practice activities, p. 120.

SUPPORT GROUP

Student Book with teacher support

Students to complete: Independent and Extended Practice activities, pp. 118–120. Check in with students as they work through the Independent Practice activities, discussing any difficulties, before supporting them to complete the Extended Practice.

EXTENSION GROUP

Student Book

Students to complete: Extended Practice activities, p. 120.

Activity sheet

Students to complete: *Activity sheet 26: Popular names*.

Practice and Mastery Book

See p. 3 for information about how to use the Practice and Mastery Book activities.

Session 4: Post-assessment

Students to complete: Post-test 20, Unit 8, Topic 1, p. 103.

Unit 8 Data representation and interpretation
Topic 2 Collecting and classifying data
Student Book pages 121–124

Learning focus

Use effective methods to record, sort and organise data, including lists and tally marks

Materials

- counters
- craft sticks or straws
- interlocking cubes (optional)
- attribute blocks
- *Activity sheet 27: Keeping track of information*

Potential difficulties: One-to-one tallying

Some students may have difficulty with transferring lists of information into tallies, as well as understanding the values of the tally marks.

- Get students to organise a collection of objects, such as counters, into categories and then count the number of items within each category. Discuss with students how a tally is a way of recording the number they have counted for each category. Work through recording one mark for one item until they have a record of each item.

- You can also get students to match a craft stick or straw to each item that they are counting, then reorganise these into a visual tally, with every fifth stick crossing the previous four.

Daily practice activity

Use everyday opportunities in the classroom to record data in simple categories, such as checking which students have returned their excursion forms or have an apple in their lunchbox or have brought in their bankbooks.

Session 1: Pre-assessment

Students to complete: Pre-test 20, Unit 8, Topic 2, p. 102.

Session 2: Topic introduction

WHOLE CLASS

Introductory activity: Exploring tally marks

Introduce the term "tally" and explain to students that this is a quick way of recording the counting of responses. Ask the class a simple question, e.g. "Do you like chocolate?" and take a quick poll. Model how to record the marks for the tally of the students' responses, paying particular attention to the fifth tally mark that crosses the others. Invite a student to count the responses for each category. Do they count the sets of tally marks by five? Display different tallies on the board and give students the opportunity to count them.

AT-STANDARD GROUP

Student Book

Students to complete: Guided and Independent Practice activities, pp. 121–123. Ask early finishers to practise sorting and tallying items in the classroom, such as counters or interlocking cubes.

SUPPORT GROUP

Concept exploration and skill development: Sorting data

To be able to gather and display data effectively, students need to develop an understanding of the ways that data can be categorised. Individually or in pairs, give students a selection of attribute blocks and ask them to sort the blocks in any way they like. Students should then organise their blocks into a 3D pictograph and make a tally of the blocks in each group. When everyone is finished, allow students time to look at each other's displays and try to work out how the blocks were classified. Were students able to sort the blocks so that each item was in a logical category?

Student Book with teacher support

Students to complete: Guided Practice activities, p. 121, using concrete materials to model the questions as required.

EXTENSION GROUP

Student Book

Students to complete: Guided and Independent Practice activities, pp. 121–123.

OXFORD UNIVERSITY PRESS

Activity sheet

Students to begin: *Activity sheet 27: Keeping track of information.*

Session 3: Instruction and consolidation

WHOLE CLASS

Topic exploration: Practising tallying

Students need plenty of practice with using tally marks in a variety of situations; the school environment provides a multitude of opportunities to do this. Take students outside and ask them to tally a particular occurrence over a fixed period of time, e.g. how many birds they see, how many cars drive by the school or the different colours of the cars. Compare the results of these tallying exercises. Did all the students record the same tallies? Why or why not? What does this reveal about data gathering?

AT-STANDARD GROUP

Teacher activity: Data collection methods

Pose the following question to students: What is the favourite drink of this group? Divide students into pairs and ask them to investigate the question. Students must record their findings in some way and present them to the group. When the activity is complete, share the different strategies implemented by students, such as using tally marks or recording answers in a list. Did students ask everyone in the group? How do they know? Based on the information, make a guide to gathering data for the whole class to use.

Student Book

Students to complete: Extended Practice activities, p. 124.

SUPPORT GROUP

Student Book with teacher support

Students to complete: Independent and Extended Practice activities, pp. 122–124. Check in with students as they work through the Independent Practice activities, discussing any difficulties, before supporting them to complete the Extended Practice.

EXTENSION GROUP

Student Book

Students to complete: Extended Practice activities, p. 124.

Activity sheet

Students to complete: *Activity sheet 27: Keeping track of information.*

Practice and Mastery Book

See p. 3 for information about how to use the Practice and Mastery Book activities.

Session 4: Post-assessment

Students to complete: Post-test 20, Unit 8, Topic 2, p. 103.

Unit 8 Data representation and interpretation

Topic 3 Representing and interpreting data

Student Book pages 125–128

Learning focus

Represent and interpret data in pictographs and tables

Materials

- *Activity sheet 28: The world's tallest*

Potential difficulties: Generating statements of findings

Generating statements about the graphs may be difficult for some students.

- Provide sentence starters or cloze sentences to assist students in developing their own sentences based on the data in tallies and graphs.
- Ensure students understand that their statements need to come directly from the data in front of them and not from other experiences or knowledge that they have relating to the topic.

Daily practice activity

Ask students to find data displays at home, such as graphs in newspapers or magazines, and bring them to class. Set aside time to share and discuss these each day, building students' knowledge of the language of data, including graph types such as bar graphs. Talk about what the graphs are showing and why they were made.

Session 1: Pre-assessment

Students to complete: Pre-test 20, Unit 8, Topic 3, p. 102.

Session 2: Topic introduction

WHOLE CLASS

Introductory activity: Creating and interpreting data displays

Tell students that they are going to form a "human pictograph" to show their favourite lunchtime activity. Start by asking one student to stand in front

of the class and give their response. Call all the other students with the same response to line up behind the first student. Repeat until all the students are lined up. Select one student to stand in front of the "graph" and discuss how easy or difficult it is to see the data in the display. Which line is the longest? Which is the shortest? Use this as a springboard to discuss graphing conventions, such as aligning pieces of data in rows to make comparison easy. Invite students to make some statements about the results, prompting them with questions if necessary.

AT-STANDARD GROUP

Student Book

Students to complete: Guided and Independent Practice activities, pp. 125–127. Instruct early finishers to ask 10 students what they did on Saturday afternoon. They should represent the results in as many different ways as possible and write two statements about what they discovered.

SUPPORT GROUP

Concept exploration and skill development: Interpreting data

Developing the language of data is a good starting point to help students interpret visual representations of information. With the students, brainstorm a list of words and phrases that can be used when interpreting tallies and graphs, e.g. less, more, least popular, most popular, favourite, survey, information, data, shows, results, findings graph, tally. In pairs, ask students to look at the first graph on p. 125 of the Student Book and generate their own statements about the data, using the words from the brainstorming activity. Scaffold as appropriate by asking questions such as, "How can you tell which response was the most popular?" Invite each pair to share one statement with the group, and ask those listening to identify the words or phrases from the brainstorming activity that were used in the statement.

Student Book with teacher support

Students to complete: Guided Practice activities, p. 125, again highlighting the key language discussed.

EXTENSION GROUP

Student Book

Students to complete: Guided and Independent Practice activities, pp. 125–127.

OXFORD UNIVERSITY PRESS

Activity sheet

Students to begin: *Activity sheet 28: The world's tallest*.

Session 3: Instruction and consolidation

WHOLE CLASS

Topic exploration: Comparing data representations

Students need lots of experience creating and interpreting data displays of different types. Conduct a quick survey on a simple topic, e.g. what pets students have, and record the results using tally marks. Divide the class into small groups; ask some groups to make a list to show the results, other groups to make a table, and the remaining groups to make a pictograph. Show the finished data displays to the class and ask students to compare them. Encourage students to consider the purpose of each method of displaying data. Which displays are the most effective for this task? In what situations would you use each method?

AT-STANDARD GROUP

Teacher activity: Graphing on a computer

To introduce students to using digital technologies to construct data displays, model the process for creating a pictograph using a table in Word, or a similar program. Start by asking the group the following question: "What is your favourite colour?" Give students a choice of five colours and record their responses with tally marks. On an interactive whiteboard or similar, choose the **Table** option from the **Insert** menu and decide on the number of rows and columns required to make the table. Demonstrate how, using the **Borders** and **Shading** tools, each cell can be shaded with a colour. Also demonstrate how to insert clip art into cells to create a pictograph. Discuss and add other important elements of a pictograph, including the title and a simple scale. In pairs, ask students to create their own simple pictograph using the same method.

Student Book

Students to complete: Extended Practice activities, p. 128.

SUPPORT GROUP

Student Book with teacher support

Students to complete: Independent and Extended Practice activities, pp. 126–128. Check in with students as they work through the Independent Practice activities, discussing any difficulties, before supporting them to complete the Extended Practice.

EXTENSION GROUP

Student Book

Students to complete: Extended Practice activities, p. 128.

Activity sheet

Students to complete: *Activity sheet 28: The world's tallest*.

Practice and Mastery Book

See p. 3 for information about how to use the Practice and Mastery Book activities.

Session 4: Post-assessment

Students to complete: Post-test 20, Unit 8, Topic 3, p. 103.

Unit 9 Chance

Topic 1 Chance

Student Book pages 129–132

Learning focus

Identify and describe chance in daily events using the language of probability

Materials

- magazines, newspapers or online resources
- A3 sheets of paper
- scissors
- glue
- a large 6-sided dice
- 6-sided dice (per pair of students)
- Unifix cubes
- a paper bag
- collection of pegs or two different varieties of chocolate bars (optional)
- *BLM 20: Probability cards*
- *Activity sheet 29: What's on for the weekend?*

Potential difficulties: Making predictions

Some students may experience difficulty in making predictions about everyday events.

- Allow students "thinking and sharing time" before they offer suggestions in whole-group situations.
- Model making a prediction to support those students who are experiencing difficulty with the language of chance, focusing on the reasoning behind the prediction.
- Encourage students to verbalise why they expect a particular outcome, linking this to previous knowledge or experiences.

Daily practice activity

Brainstorm a list of everyday activities that the students are involved in at school or at home. Each day, select an activity and ask students to indicate the likelihood that they will undertake the activity on that day. Use different methods of capturing their responses, such as students physically locating themselves on a continuum or with a show of hands for each likelihood term.

Session 1: Pre-assessment

Students to complete: Pre-test 21, Unit 9, Topic 1, p. 104.

Session 2: Topic introduction

WHOLE CLASS

Introductory activity: Chance in everyday activities

On an interactive whiteboard, display the chance terms *certain*, *impossible*, *less likely*, *most likely* and *maybe*. Explain to students that they will conduct a picture hunt using magazines, newspapers or online resources. Instruct them to find five pictures that represent something that would fit the categories of *certain*, *impossible*, *less likely*, *most likely* and *maybe* for them. Ask students to present their pictures to the class and share why they chose the items for each category, encouraging discussion. Provide students with an A3 sheet of paper and ask them to paste their pictures onto the paper and write a comment for each picture. Make a class chance booklet with their work.

AT-STANDARD GROUP

Student Book

Students to complete: Guided and Independent Practice activities, pp. 129–131. Ask early finishers to draw the same likelihood scale from p. 131 of the Student Book and place 10 events of their own choosing on the scale.

SUPPORT GROUP

Concept exploration and skill development: Assessing chance

Create cards using *BLM 20: Probability cards* and give a set to each student. Suggest an everyday situation to students and ask them to select and display the card that matches the chance of that event happening, e.g. travelling home by car on that day. Instruct students to sort themselves into groups based on their answer and discuss why they picked that particular option. Why don't all students have the same answer? Repeat with other situations and events, including some that are impossible, and discuss the students' responses. Can they offer reasonable explanations for their choices?

Student Book with teacher support

Students to complete: Guided Practice activities, p. 129, again highlighting the key language discussed.

EXTENSION GROUP

Student Book

Students to complete: Guided and Independent Practice activities, pp. 129–131.

Activity sheet

Students to begin: *Activity sheet 29: What's on for the weekend?*

Session 3: Instruction and consolidation

WHOLE CLASS

Topic exploration: Testing chance

Explain to students that when playing dice games, the number 6 is often considered the lucky number. Inform the class that, together, you want to find out if it really is. Discuss with students their thoughts on the question. Use a large 6-sided dice, or the dice on an interactive whiteboard, and roll it 10 times. Before each roll, ask some probability-related questions, e.g. "Is it impossible to roll a 1?" or "How likely is it that a 3 will be rolled?" Record the results in a table and discuss the findings. Which number came up the most? Which came up the least? Which number would you consider the luckiest? Why? To extend students' thinking, ask the class to repeat the exercise in pairs. Collect and combine the individual results to compare with the first data set. Were the results similar? Encourage students to articulate their thoughts about probability in terms of the experiment.

AT-STANDARD GROUP

Teacher activity: Experimenting with chance

Letting students observe chance at work is a good way to consolidate the concept. Display a collection of objects, such as five Unifix cubes in two different colours, and then place them in a paper bag. Explain that the objects will be randomly selected from the bag. Draw the students' attention to the proportion and chances involved in selecting a particular cube from the bag. Then ask students to consider the chances of selecting a particular cube when changes are made to the proportion, e.g. one red and four green cubes. Use the language of chance – *certain, impossible, less likely, most likely* or *maybe* – to help students understand the concept. How likely is it that a green cube will be drawn? What about the red cube? Consider conducting the activity again with other objects, such as a collection of pegs or two different varieties of chocolate bars, to check if the results are similar.

Student Book

Students to complete: Extended Practice activities, p. 132.

SUPPORT GROUP

Student Book with teacher support

Students to complete: Independent and Extended Practice activities, pp. 130–132. Check in with students as they work through the Independent Practice activities, discussing any difficulties, before supporting them to complete the Extended Practice.

EXTENSION GROUP

Student Book

Students to complete: Extended Practice activities, p. 132.

Activity sheet

Students to complete: *Activity sheet 29: What's on for the weekend?*

Practice and Mastery Book

See p. 3 for information about how to use the Practice and Mastery Book activities.

Session 4: Post-assessment

Students to complete: Post-test 21, Unit 9, Topic 1, p. 105.

1 How many?

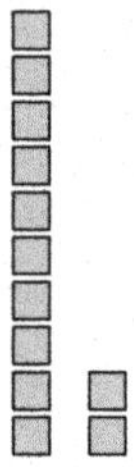

○ 10 ○ 12 ○ 14 ○ 16

2 This is 16. What is the white bead is worth?

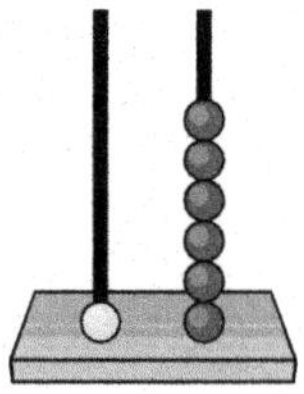

○ 6 ○ 10 ○ 1 ○ 16

3 How many? Write the number.

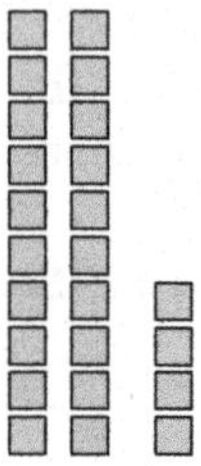

4 Write the number.

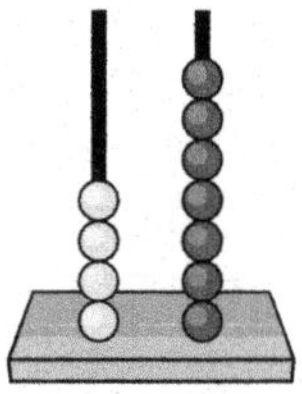

5 What are the three white beads worth?

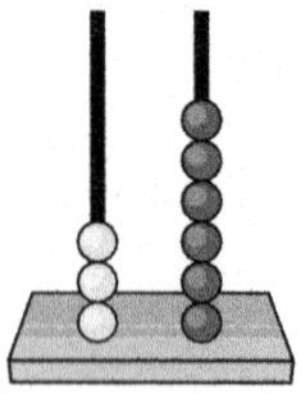

○ 30 ○ 3 ○ 13 ○ 60

6 406 can be renamed:

○ 40 tens and 6 ones.

○ 46 ones.

○ 4 ones and 6 ones.

○ 46 tens ones.

7 This is part of a hundred chart. Fill in the gaps.

	28		
		39	

8 Write the number that is:

a 1 less than 101. _____

b 10 more than 101. _____

1 How many?

○ 16　○ 20　○ 25　○ 26

2 How many?

○ 9　○ 36　○ 63　○ 26

3 Write the number.

4 Write the number.

5 What are the four black beads worth?

○ 40　○ 400　○ 4　○ 14

6 307 can be renamed:

○ 30 tens and 7 ones.

○ 37 tens and 0 ones.

○ 3 tens and 17 ones.

○ 37 ones.

7 This is part of a hundred chart. Fill in the gaps.

	55		
			67
84			

8 Use the digits to make:

5　1　8

a the largest number. _____

b the smallest number. _____

c the largest number with the 8 in the tens place. _____

1 To make 10, we add:

○ 1   ○ 2   ○ 3   ○ 4

2 3 + 4 =

○ 9   ○ 8   ○ 7   ○ 6

3 Write the answer.

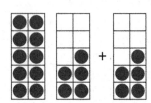

15 + 5 =

4 Write the answer.

10 + 12 =

5 The number line shows that:

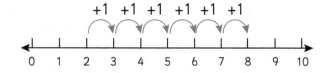

○ 1 + 5 = 6   ○ 2 + 7 = 9
○ 1 + 6 = 7   ○ 2 + 6 = 8

6 5 + 1 + 5 is the same as:

○ 5 + 5 + 5
○ 1 + 1 + 5
○ 5 + 5 + 1
○ 5 + 1 + 1

7 Show on the number line and solve.

25 + 14 =

8 Write the answer.

6 more than 38 is

1 To make 10, we add:

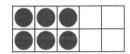

○ 3   ○ 4   ○ 5   ○ 6

2 7 + 7 =

○ 14   ○ 15   ○ 16   ○ 17

3 Write the answer.

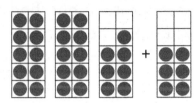

27 + 6 = ▯▯

4 Write the answer.

17 + 18 = ▯▯

5 The number line shows that:

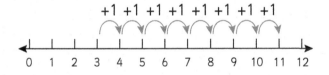

+1 +1 +1 +1 +1 +1 +1 +1

0 1 2 3 4 5 6 7 8 9 10 11 12

○ 3 + 7 = 10   ○ 4 + 7 = 11
○ 3 + 8 = 11   ○ 4 + 6 = 10

6 6 + 5 + 4 is the same as:

○ 6 + 5 + 5
○ 5 + 6 + 6
○ 6 + 4 + 5
○ 5 + 4 + 4

7 Show on the number line and solve.

⟵————————————⟶

37 + 24 = ▯▯

8 Make 3 different addition sums with these numbers: 4, 8, 6, 18.

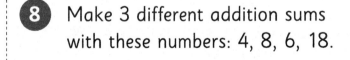

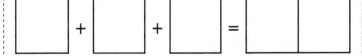

1 13 – 3 =

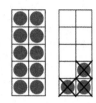

○ 11 ○ 10 ○ 9 ○ 8

2 12 – 3 is the same as:

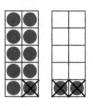

○ 12 – 2 – 2   ○ 12 – 2 – 3
○ 12 – 2 – 1   ○ 12 – 1 – 1

3 Write the answer.

16 – 7 = [ ]

4 Choose a strategy and find the answer to 24 – 9.

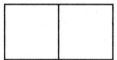

5 The number line shows that:

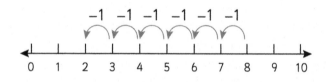

○ 8 – 5 = 3   ○ 9 – 6 = 3
○ 8 – 4 = 4   ○ 8 – 6 = 2

6 Write a subtraction fact that matches this addition fact:

3 + 9 = 12

7 What is the difference between 13 and 18?

8 Write two subtraction facts to match this addition fact:

12 + 11 = 23

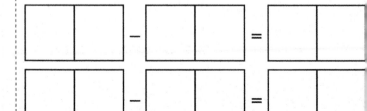

UNIT 1: TOPIC 4

1 18 − 4 =

  ○ 12 ○ 13
  ○ 14 ○ 15

2 25 − 6 is the same as:

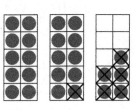

  ○ 25 − 5 − 5 ○ 25 − 5 − 1
  ○ 25 − 6 − 1 ○ 25 − 6 − 5

3 Write the answer.

27 − 8 = ☐☐

4 Choose a strategy to find the difference between 9 and 34.

☐☐

UNIT 1: TOPIC 5

5 The number line shows that:

−1 −1 −1 −1 −1 −1 −1

0 1 2 3 4 5 6 7 8 9 10 11 12 13

  ○ 11 − 7 = 4 ○ 12 − 6 = 6
  ○ 11 − 5 = 6 ○ 12 − 7 = 5

6 Write a subtraction fact that matches this addition fact:

17 + 9 = 26

☐☐ − ☐ = ☐

7 Show on the number line and solve.

35 − 16 = ☐☐

8 Write two subtraction facts to match this addition fact:

23 + 14 = 37

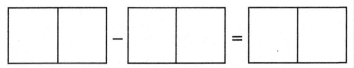

1 The frog will skip by:

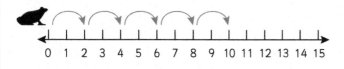

- ⃝ 2s
- ⃝ 4s
- ⃝ 3s
- ⃝ 5s

2 Look at question 1. After 10, the frog will land on:

⃝ 11   ⃝ 12   ⃝ 13   ⃝ 14

3 2 + 2 + 2 = 6

Which of these also counts the beads?

- ⃝ two 2s are 4
- ⃝ three 2s are 6
- ⃝ four 2s are 8
- ⃝ three 3s are 9

4 Fill in the blanks.

3	+	3	=	[ ]
[ ]	3s are	[ ]
[ ]	×	[ ]	=	[ ]

5 Fill in the blanks.

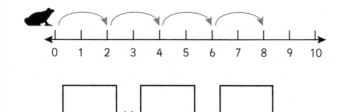

[ ] × [ ] = [ ]

6 Show on the number line and solve.

7 × 2 = [ ]

7 Write a multiplication sentence.

[ ] × [ ] = [ ]

8 Write a multiplication sentence.

[ ] × [ ] = [ ]

1 The frog will skip by:

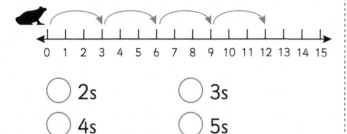

0 1 2 3 4 5 6 7 8 9 10 11 12 13 14 15

○ 2s   ○ 3s

○ 4s   ○ 5s

2 Look at question 1. After 12, the frog will land on:

○ 13   ○ 14   ○ 15   ○ 16

---

3 3 + 3 + 3 + 3 = 12

Which of these also counts the beads?

○ six 2s are 6

○ three 3s are 9

○ four 2s are 8

○ four 3s are 12

4 Fill in the blanks.

| 4 | + | | + | | = | | |

| | | 4s are | | | |

| | × | | = | | |

---

5 Write the equation.

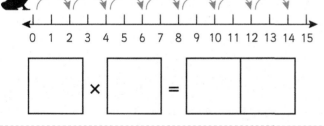

0 1 2 3 4 5 6 7 8 9 10 11 12 13 14 15

| | × | | = | | |

6 Show on the number line and solve.

4 x 3 = | |

0 1 2 3 4 5 6 7 8 9 10 11 12 13 14 15

---

7 Draw the array. Write the answer.

4 x 6 = | |

8 Draw 2 different arrays with 8 counters. Write in the boxes.

| | × | | = 8 | | × | | = 8

1 Draw circles to make equal groups of 2.

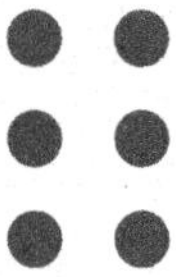

● ●
● ●
● ●

2 Look at question 1.

6 split into groups of 2 =

◯ 1 group.   ◯ 2 groups.
◯ 3 groups. ◯ 4 groups.

3 Draw circles to make equal groups of 3.

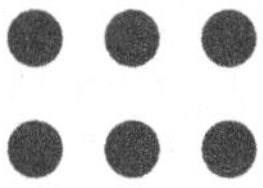

● ● ●
● ● ●

4 Look at question 3.

6 split into groups of 3 is ☐

5 Can 7 split into equal groups of 2?

● ● ● ● ● ● ●

◯ Yes   ◯ No

6 Can 10 split into equal groups of 3?

● ● ● ● ● ● ● ● ● ●

◯ Yes   ◯ No

7 Look at the dots. You can make equal groups of:

● ● ● ● ● ● ● ● ● ●

◯ 2 and 3   ◯ 2 and 4
◯ 2 and 5   ◯ 2 and 6

8 The dots can be shared equally between:

● ● ● ● ● ● ● ●

◯ 2 or 3 people.
◯ 2 or 4 people.
◯ 3 or 4 people.
◯ 3 or 5 people.

1 Draw circles to make equal groups of 2.

2 Look at question 1.

10 divided into groups of 2 =

○ 3 groups.   ○ 4 groups.
○ 5 groups.   ○ 6 groups.

3 Draw circles to make equal groups of 4.

4 Look at question 3.

16 divided into 4s is ☐

$16 \div 4 =$ ☐

5 Make groups of 2.

Are the shares equal or unequal?

○ Equal   ○ Unequal

6 Make groups of 3.

Are the shares equal or unequal?

○ Equal   ○ Unequal

7 What can you make equal groups of? Shade the circles.

○ 2   ○ 3   ○ 4   ○ 5

8 The dots can be shared equally between:

○ 2 or 3 people.   ○ 3 or 4 people.
○ 2 or 5 people.   ○ 3 or 5 people.

1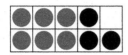

$6 + 3 = \boxed{}$

2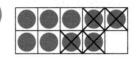

$9 - 4 = \boxed{}$

3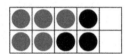

$\boxed{} + \boxed{} = \boxed{}$

4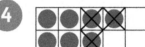

$\boxed{} - \boxed{} = \boxed{}$

5 $8 + 2 = \boxed{}$

6 $10 - 6 = \boxed{}$

7 49 + 49 is:

○ 100.

○ more than 100.

○ less than 100.

8 41 + 39 is:

○ bigger than 40 + 40.

○ the same as 40 + 40.

○ smaller than 40 + 40.

1

$\boxed{} + \boxed{} = \boxed{}\boxed{}$

2

$\boxed{}\boxed{} - \boxed{} = \boxed{}\boxed{}$

3 3 + 8 = $\boxed{}$

4 14 − 6 = $\boxed{}$

5 15 + 4 = $\boxed{}$

6 18 − 6 = $\boxed{}$

7 149 + 99 is:

○ more than 150.

○ 150.

○ less than 150.

8 Choose the best estimate.

121 − 49 is:

○ close to 90.

○ close to 80.

○ close to 70.

1 What is the shaded part?

○ a whole ○ a half ○ a quarter

2 What is a way to write a half?

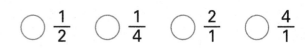

○ $\frac{1}{2}$ ○ $\frac{1}{4}$ ○ $\frac{2}{1}$ ○ $\frac{4}{1}$

3 Shade $\frac{1}{4}$ of the circle.

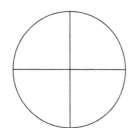

4 Write in the box. What fraction is shaded?

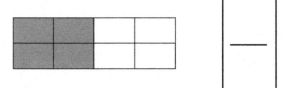

UNIT 2: TOPIC 2

5 Colour $\frac{1}{2}$ of the stars.

6 What fraction is shaded?

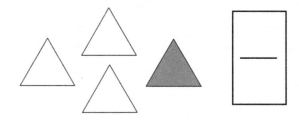

7 Colour $\frac{1}{4}$ of the circles.

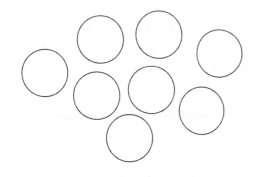

8 **a** Colour $\frac{1}{2}$ red.

b Colour $\frac{1}{4}$ blue.

c What fraction is white? _____

1 What is the shaded part?

- ○ $\frac{1}{2}$
- ○ $\frac{1}{4}$
- ○ $\frac{1}{8}$
- ○ whole

2 Shade $\frac{1}{8}$ of the rectangle.

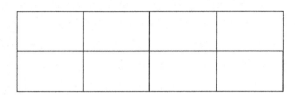

3 Shade $\frac{1}{4}$ of the circle.

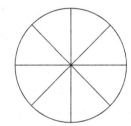

4 Which list goes from smallest to biggest?

- ○ $\frac{1}{2}, \frac{1}{4}, \frac{1}{8}$
- ○ $\frac{1}{4}, \frac{1}{8}, \frac{1}{2}$
- ○ $\frac{1}{8}, \frac{1}{2}, \frac{1}{4}$
- ○ $\frac{1}{8}, \frac{1}{4}, \frac{1}{2}$

5 Colour $\frac{1}{2}$ of the stars.

6 What fraction is shaded?

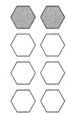 

7 Colour $\frac{1}{2}$ of the circles.

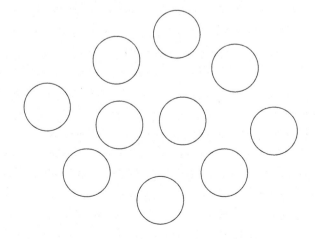

8
  a Colour $\frac{1}{8}$ green.

  b Colour $\frac{1}{2}$ red.

  c Colour $\frac{1}{4}$ blue.

  d What fraction is white? _____

1 How many 10c coins do you need to make 20c?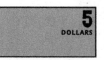

○ 1   ○ 2   ○ 3   ○ 4

2 How many $5 notes do you need to make $20?

○ 2   ○ 3   ○ 4   ○ 5

3 Write on the coins. Which three coins make 50c?

4 Write on the notes. How could you change $50 for three notes?

5 How much is this?

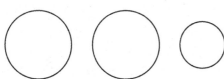

○ 25c   ○ 35c
○ 45c   ○ 50c

6 How much is this?

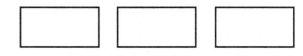

○ $30   ○ $40
○ $45   ○ $50

7 Draw 3 coins that make 70c.

8 What is the least number of notes and coins that you could use to make $29? Draw them.

1 How many 5c coins do you need to make 20c?

○ 1 ○ 2 ○ 3 ○ 4

2 How many $10 notes do you need to make $50?

○ 2 ○ 5 ○ 10 ○ 20

3 Write on the coins. Which four coins have the same value as $1?

4 Write on the notes. How could you change $100 for five notes?

UNIT 3: TOPIC 2

5 How much is this?

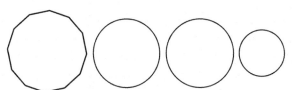

○ 65c ○ 75c
○ 85c ○ 95c

6 How much is this?

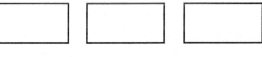

○ $91 ○ $96
○ $82 ○ $86

7 Draw 3 coins that make $1.05.

8 What is the least number of notes and coins that you could use to make $149? Draw them.

1 What is the missing number?

0	2	4		8	10

○ 4 ○ 5 ○ 6 ○ 7

2 How many do the numbers go down by?

20	18	16	14	12	10

○ 1 ○ 2 ○ 3 ○ 4

3 What is the next number in the pattern?

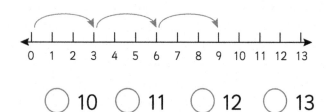

○ 10 ○ 11 ○ 12 ○ 13

4 If the numbers in a pattern end in 5, then 0, then 5, then 0, then 5, then 0, you would be counting by:

○ 2 ○ 3 ○ 4 ○ 5

5 Sam has 2 toys. He gets 1 more. Which number sentence matches the story?

○ 2 + 2 = 4   ○ 2 + 1 = 3
○ 2 − 2 = 0   ○ 2 − 1 = 1

6 Write a number sentence for this story. Emma has 3 toys. She loses 2.

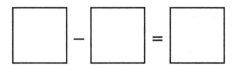

7 Jack has $10. He spends $3. How much does he have left?

_____

Is this addition or subtraction?

○ Addition   ○ Subtraction

8 Lucy has 9 marbles. She loses 3. How many does she have left? Write a number sentence to show the answer.

_____

1 Fill in the blanks in this counting pattern.

0	2	4		8	10		14

2 The numbers go down by:

30	27	24	21	18	15	12	9

○ 2   ○ 3   ○ 4   ○ 5

3 Fill in the blanks for this pattern.

2	6	10		18	22		

4 If the last digit in a pattern was:

3, 8, 3, 8, 3, 8

you would be counting by:

○ 2   ○ 3   ○ 4   ○ 5

5 Sam has 7 toys. He loses 2. Which number sentence matches the story?

○ 7 + 2 = 9
○ 7 + 3 = 10
○ 7 − 2 = 5
○ 7 − 7 = 0

6 Tom has 5 cars. He gets 4 more. Write a number sentence for the story.

$$\boxed{} + \boxed{} = \boxed{}$$

7 Eva has $25. She spends $13. How much does she have left?

_____

Did you add or subtract?

○ Added   ○ Subtracted

8 Tran reads 11 pages at school. He reads 8 pages at home. How many pages does he read altogether? Write a number sentence to show the answer.

_____

1 How many hand spans long is the line?

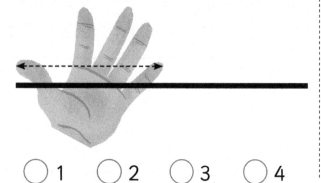

○ 1   ○ 2   ○ 3   ○ 4

2 The area of the paper is about:

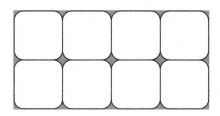

○ 6 tiles.   ○ 7 tiles.
○ 8 tiles.   ○ 9 tiles.

3 How many finger lengths is the pencil?

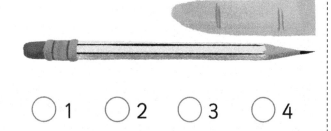

○ 1   ○ 2   ○ 3   ○ 4

4 The paper has 3 erasers on it. A good estimate for the area is:

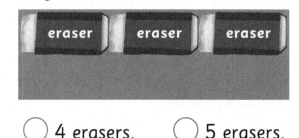

○ 4 erasers.   ○ 5 erasers.
○ 6 erasers.   ○ 8 erasers.

5 How tall is your classroom door?

○ more than 1 metre
○ about 1 metre
○ less than 1 metre

6 Which is less than 1 metre long?

○ a classroom   ○ a train
○ a horse   ○ a cat

7 Which of these is more than 1 metre long?

○ a pencil   ○ a foot
○ an ant   ○ a school hall

8 What is something that is about 1 metre long?

_____

1 How many fingers long is the line?

○ 1   ○ 2   ○ 3   ○ 4

2 A good estimate for the area of the paper is:

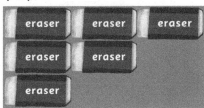

○ 6 erasers.   ○ 7 erasers.
○ 8 erasers.   ○ 9 erasers.

3 How many foot lengths is the doorway?

○ 2   ○ 4   ○ 6   ○ 8

4 Use a unit of your choice to find the area of the shape.

The area is: _____

5 Is the length of your hand:

○ more than 1 metre?
○ about 1 metre?
○ less than 1 metre?

6 Choose the best estimate for the length of a bed.

○ 1 centimetre   ○ 1 metre
○ 2 centimetres   ○ 2 metres

7 What is the length of the black line?

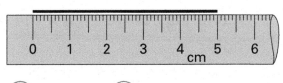

○ 4 m   ○ 5 m
○ 4 cm   ○ 5 cm

8 Use a ruler to measure this line. Write the answer.

1 How many cubes would you need to make this?

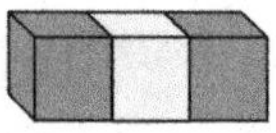

- ◯ 2 cubes
- ◯ 4 cubes
- ◯ 3 cubes
- ◯ 5 cubes

2 What is the volume of this?

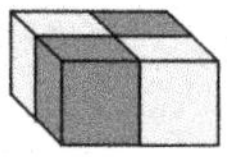

◻ cubes

3 Which is true?

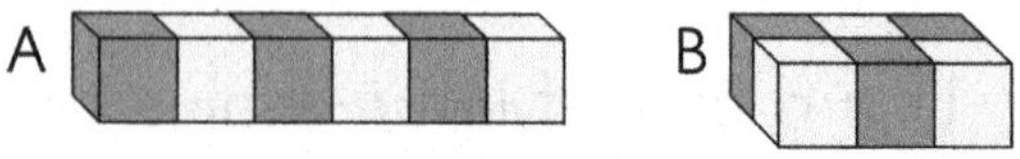

A B

- ◯ A has a bigger volume than B.
- ◯ A has the same volume as B.
- ◯ A has a smaller volume than B.

4 From smallest to largest volume, the order is:

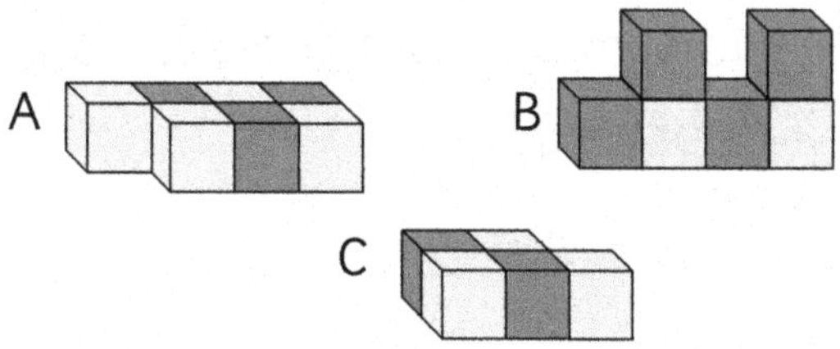

- ◯ A, B, C.
- ◯ A, C, B.
- ◯ C, A, B.
- ◯ C, B, A.

5 Which holds the most water?

bowl   glass   jug

- ◯ the jug
- ◯ the bowl
- ◯ the glass

6 Look at question 5. Which is true?

- ◯ The jug holds the least.
- ◯ The glass holds less than the jug.
- ◯ The glass holds more than the bowl.

7 Look at question 5. Write the objects in order from smallest to largest capacity.

_____

_____

8 Look at question 5. About how many jugs of water will the bowl hold?

- ◯ 1
- ◯ 3
- ◯ 30
- ◯ 100

1 How many cubes would you need to make this?

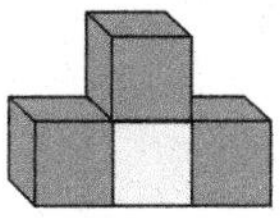

- ◯ 2 cubes   ◯ 3 cubes
- ◯ 4 cubes   ◯ 5 cubes

2 What is the volume of this?

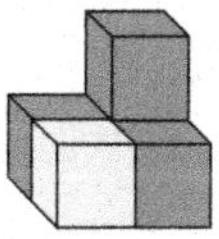

☐ cubes

3 Which sentence is true?

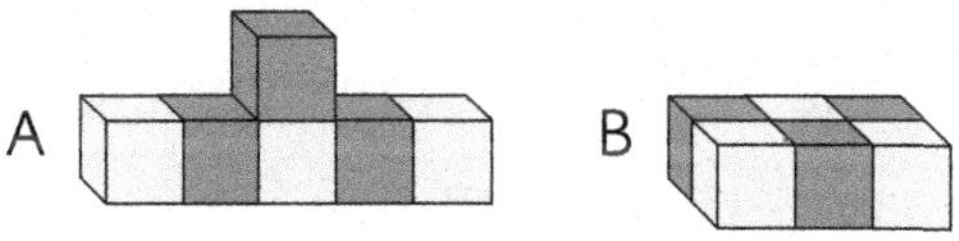

A   B

- ◯ A has a bigger volume than B.
- ◯ A has the same volume as B.
- ◯ A has a smaller volume than B.

4 From smallest to largest volume, the order is:

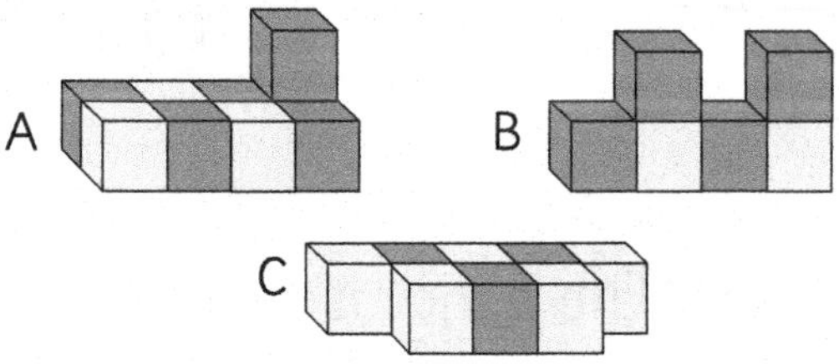

A   B

C

- ◯ B, C, A.   ◯ C, A, B.
- ◯ A, C, B.   ◯ C, B, A.

5 Which holds the most water?

spoon   **glass**   **bucket**   **jug**

- ◯ The jug   ◯ The bucket
- ◯ The glass   ◯ The spoon

6 Look at question 5. Which is true?

- ◯ The jug has the largest capacity.
- ◯ The glass holds less than the spoon.
- ◯ The spoon has the smallest capacity.
- ◯ The jug holds more than the bucket.

7 Look at question 5. Write the objects in order from smallest to largest capacity.

_____

_____

8 Look at question 5. About how many glasses of water will the jug hold?

◯ 1   ◯ 4   ◯ 20   ◯ 40

1 The mouse is:

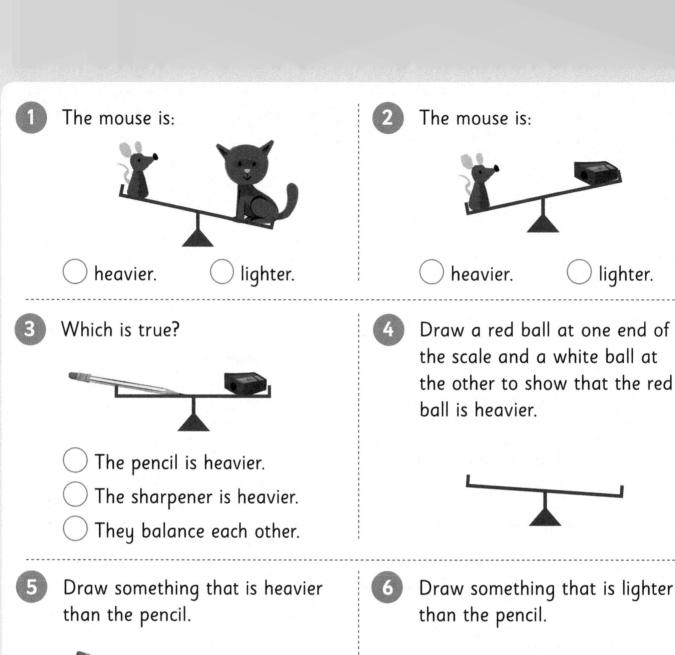

○ heavier.   ○ lighter.

2 The mouse is:

○ heavier.   ○ lighter.

3 Which is true?

○ The pencil is heavier.
○ The sharpener is heavier.
○ They balance each other.

4 Draw a red ball at one end of the scale and a white ball at the other to show that the red ball is heavier.

5 Draw something that is heavier than the pencil.

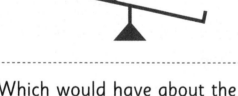

6 Draw something that is lighter than the pencil.

7 Which would have about the same mass as you?

○ a cat   ○ a horse
○ a big dog   ○ a mouse

8 Write the labels of the objects (A, B and C) in order from lightest to heaviest.

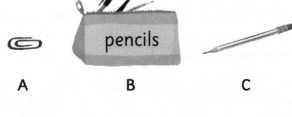

A   B   C

_____

1 Which is true?

- ○ The mouse is heavier.
- ○ The teddy is heavier.
- ○ They are both the same.

2 Which has the smaller mass?

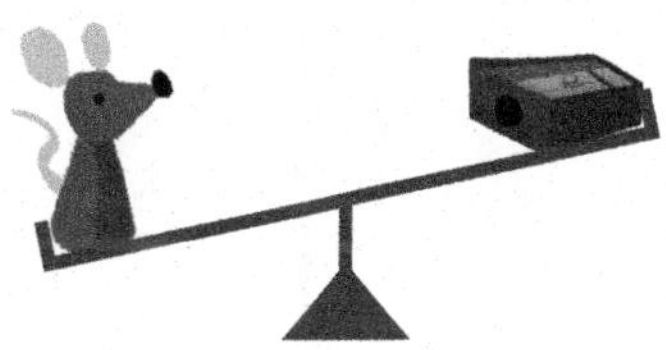

- ○ The sharpener
- ○ The mouse

3 Which is true?

- ○ The teddy is heavier.
- ○ The cat is heavier.
- ○ They are both the same.

4 The ball has a bigger mass than the sharpener. Draw one at each end of the balance scale.

5 Which is true?

- ○ The white ball is much heavier.
- ○ They have exactly the same mass.
- ○ They have almost the same mass.

6 Which is true?

- ○ They have almost the same mass.
- ○ The pencil case is much heavier.

7 Which has about the same mass as a shoe?

- ○ an eraser
- ○ a person
- ○ a book
- ○ a chair

8 Order the objects (A, B, C and D) from lightest to heaviest.

A   B   C   D

_____

1 The time is:

- ○ 12 o'clock.
- ○ 6 o'clock.
- ○ 7 o'clock.

2 The time is:

- ○ half past 6.
- ○ half past 3.
- ○ half past 4.

3 The time is half past 8. Draw the minute hand on the clock.

4 The time is half past 5. Draw the time on the clock.

UNIT 5: TOPIC 7

5 The first month of the year is:

- ○ May.
- ○ January.
- ○ June.

6 The season that comes after spring is:

- ○ summer.
- ○ autumn.
- ○ winter.

7 May has 31:

- ○ hours.
- ○ weeks.
- ○ days.
- ○ months.

8 February has 4:

- ○ hours.
- ○ weeks.
- ○ days.
- ○ months.

1 At 3 o'clock the minute hand points to the:

○ 6 ○ 12 ○ 3 ○ 9

2 The time is:

○ half past 6. ○ half past 9.
○ half past 8.

3 The time is quarter past 10. Draw the minute hand on the clock.

4 The time is quarter to 4. Draw the time on the clock.

5 The month that comes after April is:

○ May. ○ March.
○ June.

6 Tran lives in Sydney.
His birthday is in December.
His birthday is in:

○ spring. ○ summer.
○ autumn. ○ winter.

7 There are three months that begin with 'J'. Write the months in the order that they occur in the year.

_____

_____

8 Look at question 6.
Melbourne's winter months are:

○ April, May and June.
○ January, February and March.
○ June, July and August.
○ August, September and October.

1 A month lasts:

◯ about four weeks.
◯ about five weeks.
◯ exactly three weeks.

2 In one day, there are:

◯ 24 hours.
◯ 20 hours.
◯ 12 hours.

3 An hour lasts:

◯ 10 minutes.
◯ 50 minutes.
◯ 60 minutes.

4 30 minutes is the same as:

◯ half an hour.
◯ an hour.
◯ two hours.

5 How many seconds are in one minute?

◯ 60
◯ 30
◯ 10

6 The last month of the year is:

◯ May.
◯ December.
◯ June.

7 A school day lasts:

◯ a few seconds.
◯ a few minutes.
◯ a few hours.

8 To write the word "fun" takes:

◯ a few seconds.
◯ a few minutes.
◯ a few hours.

1 48 hours is the same as:

- ◯ 1 day.
- ◯ 2 days.
- ◯ 3 days.
- ◯ 4 days.

2 At night, we usually sleep for about:

- ◯ 1 to 3 hours.
- ◯ 7 to 10 hours.
- ◯ 20 to 24 hours.
- ◯ 30 to 40 hours.

3 Two minutes is the same as:

- ◯ 30 seconds.
- ◯ 60 seconds.
- ◯ 120 seconds.
- ◯ 200 seconds.

4 24 months is the same as:

- ◯ one year.
- ◯ one and a half years.
- ◯ two years.
- ◯ two and a half years.

5 It takes less than 10 seconds to:

- ◯ have a shower.
- ◯ write the word "time".
- ◯ sing 10 songs.
- ◯ read all the books in the library.

6 It takes a few minutes to:

- ◯ eat an apple.
- ◯ eat a grape.
- ◯ take a sip of water.
- ◯ grow a flower.

7 How many seconds have passed?

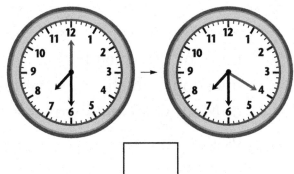

8 Draw the second clock to show that 50 seconds have passed.

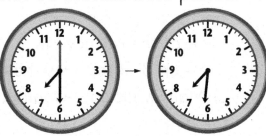

1 In a year, there are:

○ 7 months.

○ 10 months.

○ 12 months.

2 What is the last month of the year?

○ May   ○ January

○ December   ○ October

3 How many Saturdays are there in this month? Write the answer.

Sun	Mon	Tue	Wed	Thu	Fri	Sat
				1	2	3
4	5	6	7	8	9	10
11	12	13	14	15	16	17
18	19	20	21	22	23	24
25	26	27	28	29	30	31

4 Look at the calendar in question 3. On what day is the 12th?

○ Sunday

○ Monday

○ Tuesday

○ Wednesday

5 Look at the calendar in question 3. What date is it a week after the 13th?

○ 19th   ○ 20th

○ 21st   ○ 22nd

6 Look at the calendar in question 3. Three days after the 11th, the day is:

○ Monday.   ○ Tuesday.

○ Wednesday.   ○ Thursday.

7 Look at the calendar in question 3. If this was the month of May, what date would it be the day after the 31st?

_____

8 Look at the calendar in question 3. If this was the month of May, what date was the day before the 1st?

_____

Oxford Mathematics Primary Years Programme Year 2 © Oxford University Press 2019. This sheet may be photocopied for non-commercial classroom use

1 In January, there are:

○ 28 days.

○ 30 days.

○ 31 days.

2 Could this calendar month be for June?

Sun	Mon	Tue	Wed	Thu	Fri	Sat
				1	2	3
4	5	6	7	8	9	10
11	12	13	14	15	16	17
18	19	20	21	22	23	24
25	26	27	28	29	30	31

○ Yes   ○ No

3 Which of these months have the same number of days?

○ March and April

○ April and May

○ May and June

○ July and August

4 Look at the calendar in question 2. Which days are there five of in the month?

○ Monday, Tuesday, Wednesday

○ Wednesday, Thursday, Friday

○ Thursday, Friday, Saturday

○ Friday, Saturday, Sunday

5 Which month never has more than 29 days?

○ February   ○ March

○ May   ○ June

6 Look at the calendar in question 2. On what date is the first Wednesday of the month?

_____

7 Look at the calendar in question 2. If this was December, what was the date the day before December 1st?

_____

8 Look at the calendar in question 2. If this was December, what would be the day and date 12 days after December 25th?

_____

1 How many corners does this shape have?

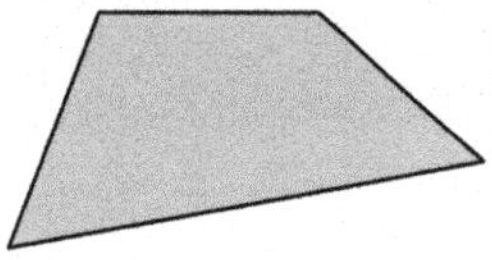

○ 1 ○ 2 ○ 3 ○ 4

2 How many sides does this shape have?

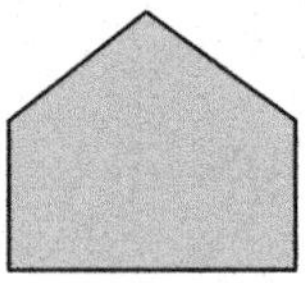

○ 2 ○ 3 ○ 4 ○ 5

3 This is a:

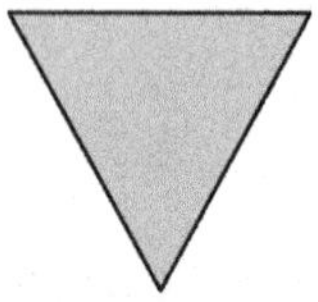

○ quadrilateral. ○ triangle.
○ pentagon. ○ hexagon.

4 This is a:

○ hexagon. ○ triangle.
○ pentagon. ○ rectangle.

5 How many straight sides does this shape have?

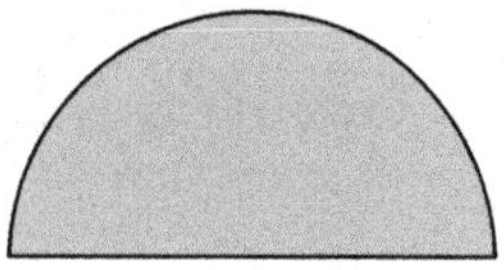

○ 0 ○ 1 ○ 2

6 How many straight sides does this shape have?

○ 0 ○ 1 ○ 2

7 **a** Pentagon or hexagon?

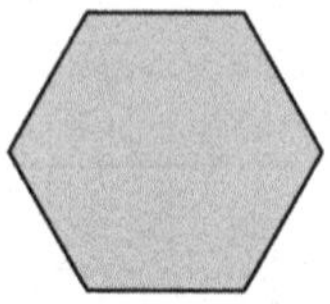

_____

b The shape has ☐ sides

and ☐ corners.

8 Draw a shape with 5 straight sides and 5 corners.

1 Is the arrow pointing to a side or a corner?

2 Is the arrow pointing to a side or a corner?

3 A pentagon has:

[ ] sides and [ ] corners.

4 A hexagon has:

[ ] sides and [ ] corners.

5 This shape has:

○ 2 straight sides.

○ no straight sides.

○ a curved side and a straight side.

6 This shape has:

○ 2 straight sides.

○ no straight sides.

○ 2 curved sides.

7 **a** Octagon or hexagon?

_____

b The shape has [ ] sides and [ ] corners.

8 **a** Draw a shape with 4 straight sides that are all the same length.

b The shape is a _____ .

1 Is the arrow pointing to a face?

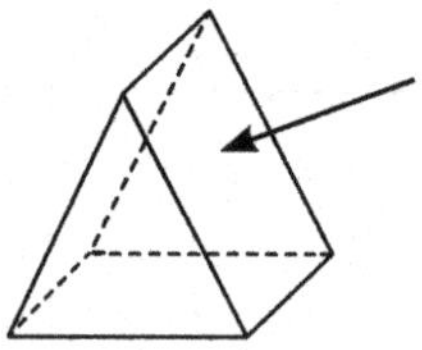

○ Yes
○ No

2 Is the arrow pointing to an edge?

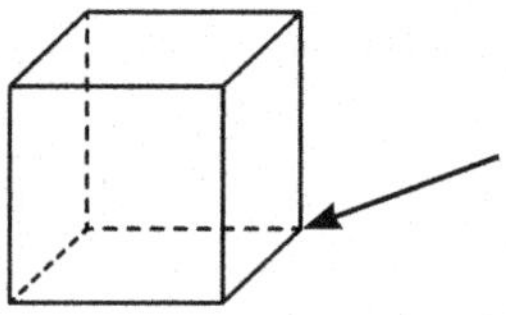

○ Yes
○ No

3 How many edges are there on a sphere?

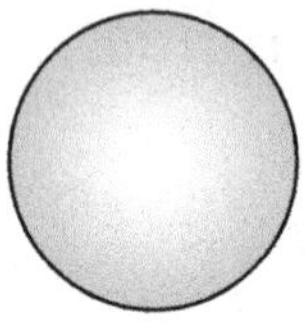

○ 2   ○ 1   ○ 0

4 How many faces are there on a cube?

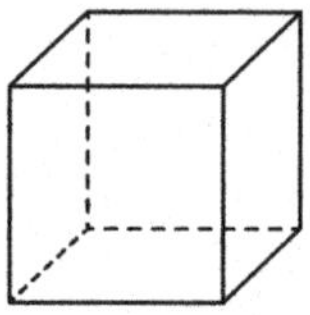

○ 4   ○ 5   ○ 6   ○ 7

5 This shape has:

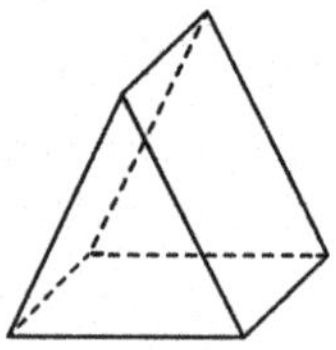

○ 5 faces.   ○ 4 faces.
○ 3 faces.

6 This shape has:

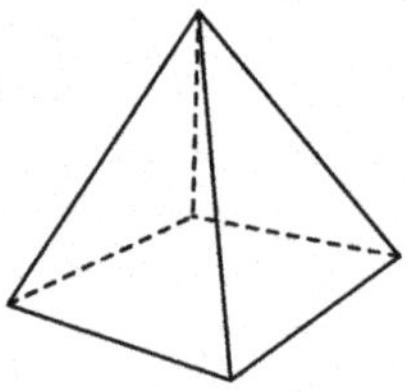

○ 4 corners.   ○ 5 corners.
○ 6 corners.

7 What am I? I have no flat faces. I am a:

○ sphere. 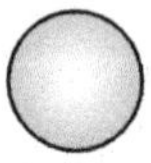
○ cone. 
○ cylinder.

8 What am I? I have 2 flat faces and 1 curved face. I am a:

○ sphere. 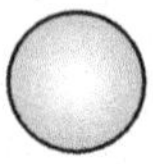
○ cone. 
○ cylinder.

1 Write the answer in the box. Is this an edge, a face or a corner?

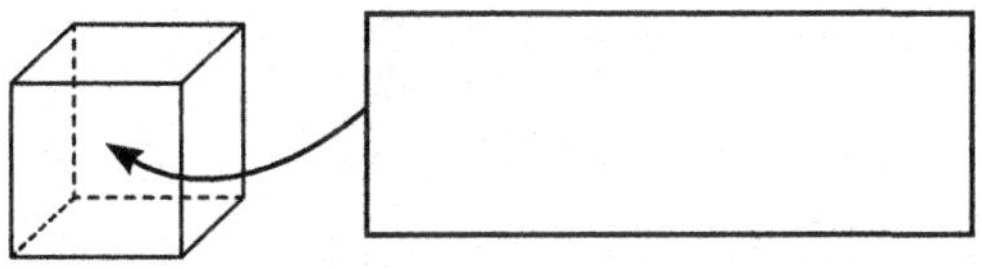

2 Write the answer in the box. Is this an edge, a face or a corner?

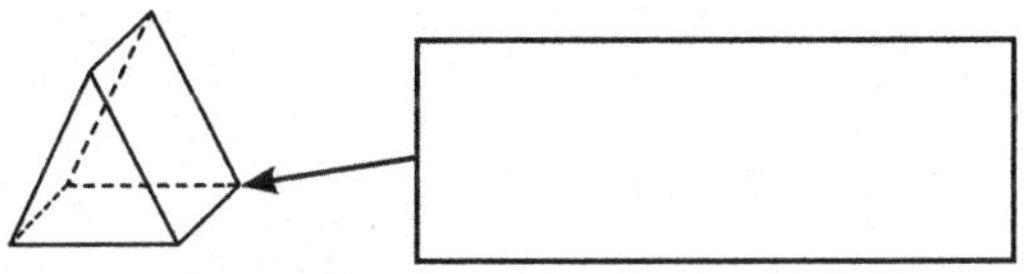

3 How many edges does this shape have?

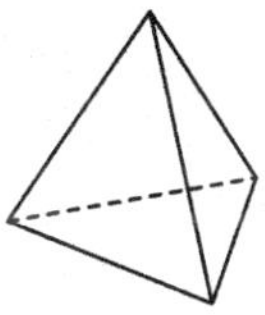

◯ 3 ◯ 4 ◯ 5 ◯ 6

4 How many faces does this shape have?

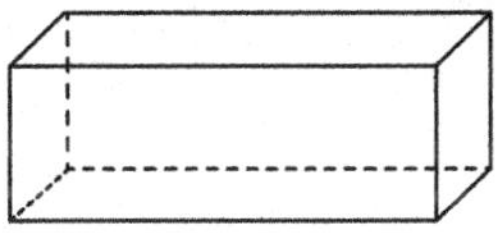

◯ 4 ◯ 5 ◯ 6 ◯ 7

5 This shape has:

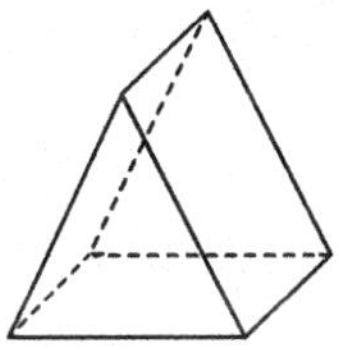

◯ 5 faces and 5 corners.
◯ 5 faces and 6 corners.
◯ 6 faces and 5 corners.

6 This shape has:

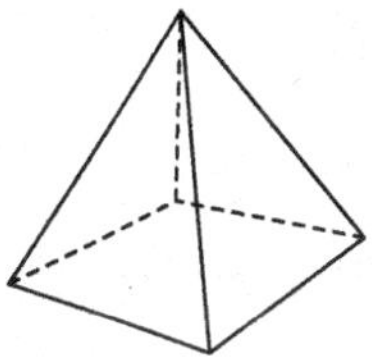

◯ 4 faces and 4 corners.
◯ 5 faces and 5 corners.
◯ 5 faces and 4 corners.

7 Look at the shape in question 5.

a Is it a prism or a pyramid?

_____

b The shape is made up of

☐ rectangles and

☐ triangles.

8 Look at the shape in question 3.

a Is it a prism or a pyramid?

_____

b The shape is made up of

☐ rectangles and

☐ triangles.

1 Draw a star in the empty box on the bottom row.

2 Look at question 1. Draw a smiley face above the cap.

3 Look at question 1. What is next to the smiley face?

○ the teddy   ○ the star

○ the shoe   ○ the cap

4 Look at question 1. What is below the shoe?

○ the teddy   ○ the star

○ the cap

5 Look at question 1. Which box is empty?

○ the one above the hat

○ the one above the shoe

○ the one above the star

○ the one above the teddy

6 Look at question 1.

a Draw a flower in the empty box.

b Write the answer. What is below the flower?

_____

7 Write the answer. What am I?

I am above the teddy and next to the shoe.

I am the _____ .

8 Write the answer. What am I?

I am between the teddy and the cap.

I am the _____ .

1 Draw a star in the centre box.

2 Look at question 1. What is in the bottom left box?

○ the shoe   ○ the cap

○ the dog   ○ the rabbit

3 Look at question 1. Draw a smiley face in the top right box.

4 Look at question 1. The star is next to:

○ the cap and the teddy.

○ the teddy and the rabbit.

○ the dog and the shoe.

○ the cap and the smiley face.

5 Look at question 1. What is on the top row, in the middle?

○ the cap   ○ the rabbit

○ the teddy   ○ the star

6 **a** Look at question 1. The empty box on the top row is on the:

○ left.   ○ right.   ○ middle.

b Draw a hand in this empty box.

7 Look at question 1. Fill in the gaps using words like "above", "next to" and "below".

The rabbit is _____

the star and _____

the shoe.

8 Look at question 1.

a Where is the empty box?

_____

_____

b Draw a flower in the empty box.

1 Forwards or backwards?

◯ Forwards ◯ Backwards

2 Forwards or backwards?

◯ Forwards ◯ Backwards

3 The face is where you are. Move backwards 3 squares. Move down 1 square. Where are you?

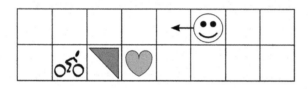

◯ the bike ◯ the triangle

◯ the heart

4 You are on the bike. To get to the heart, you go:

◯ forwards 3 squares and up 3 squares.

◯ forwards 2 squares and up 3 squares.

◯ forwards 3 squares and up 2 squares.

UNIT 7: TOPIC 3

5 Is the turn clockwise or anticlockwise?

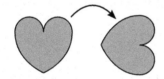

◯ Clockwise ◯ Anticlockwise

6 Which way should the dog go to fetch the shoe?

◯ Clockwise ◯ Anticlockwise

7 The face is you. If you go 4 places clockwise, you will be at the:

_____

8 Look at question 7. The face is you. If you go 5 places anticlockwise, you will be at the:

_____

1 Slide or flip?

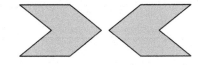

○ Slide   ○ Flip

2 What happened?

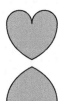

○ horizontal flip

○ vertical flip

3 Make a pattern by sliding the shape horizontally three times.

4 Make a pattern by flipping the shape horizontally and vertically.

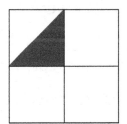

5 Half turn or quarter turn?

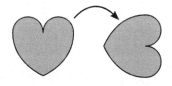

○ half turn

○ quarter turn

6 What sort of turn?

○ half turn

○ quarter turn to the left

○ quarter turn to the right

7 Draw the shape after a quarter turn to the left.

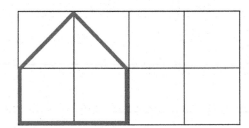

8 Turn the face a quarter turn to the right each time to make a pattern.

1 Tran wrote a tick for each sticker he got. How many stickers did he get?

✓ ✓ ✓ ✓ ✓ ✓ ✓

○ 5   ○ 6   ○ 7   ○ 8

3 Tran wanted to know which pet people like. He asked 12 friends. The answers were:

dog, dog, cat, dog, fish, cat, fish, dog, dog, cat, cat, dog

Put a tick for each one.

Pet		Ticks
Dog 		
Cat 		
Fish 		

5 Make a pictograph using the data in questions 3 and 4.

6			
5			
4			
3			
2			
1	 🐕		
	Dog	Cat	Fish

2 Write a tick for every letter in the word "Wednesday".

_____

4 Look at the data in question 3. Write the numbers in the table.

Pet		Total
Dog		
Cat		
Fish		

6 How many people like cats best?

○ 2   ○ 3   ○ 4

7 How many more people chose dogs than fish?

○ 2   ○ 3   ○ 4

8 What question do you think Tran asked the 12 people?

_____

_____

_____

1 Jack tallied the number of stickers he got. Fill in the totals.

Day	Tally	Total
Monday	III	
Tuesday	JHT	
Wednesday	JHT I	
Thursday	IIII	
Friday	III	

2 Look at the table in question 1. The day Jack got the most stickers was:

◯ Monday.   ◯ Tuesday.

◯ Wednesday.   ◯ Thursday.

3 Finish the graph for Tuesday.

The number of stickers Jack got

(◉◉) = 1 sticker

6		
5		
4		
3	◉◉	
2	◉◉	
1	◉◉	
	Mon	Tues

4 Finish the graph for Wednesday, Thursday and Friday.

The number of stickers Jack got

(◉◉) =
1 sticker

6			
5			
4			
3			
2			
1			
	Wed	Thurs	Fri

5 Look at the graphs. How many more stickers did Jack get on Wednesday than Monday?

_____

6 How many stickers did Jack get in the whole week?

_____

7 Next week, Jack will get 4 more stickers each day than he did the week before. Fill in the table.

Day	Tally	Total
Monday		
Tuesday		
Wednesday		
Thursday		
Friday		

8 Draw a pictograph using the data in question 7.

The number of stickers Jack will get

(◉◉) =
1 sticker

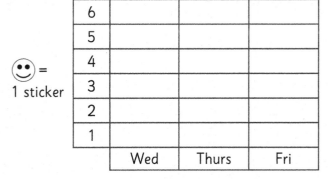

1					
	Mon	Tues	Wed	Thurs	Fri

1 What is the chance that a cat will sit next to you in class today?

◯ Certain   ◯ Impossible

2 What is the chance that you will come to school next year?

◯ Certain   ◯ Impossible

3 What is the chance that it will rain next week?

◯ Certain
◯ Maybe
◯ Impossible

4 What is the chance that you will get all these questions right?

◯ Certain
◯ Maybe
◯ Impossible

5 Choose something that is **certain** to happen.

◯ I will be on TV.
◯ I will read next week.
◯ I will run from here to the Moon.

6 Choose something that is **impossible** to happen.

◯ I will ride on a train one day.
◯ I will run around Australia backwards.
◯ I will go to my friend's house.

7 What is something that might happen?

_____

_____

_____

_____

_____

8 What is something that will not happen?

_____

_____

_____

_____

1 What is the chance that a pig will sing in class today?

○ Certain ○ Impossible

2 What is the chance that someone will talk today?

○ Certain ○ Impossible

3 What is the chance that the sun will shine next week?

○ Certain ○ Likely
○ Unlikely ○ Impossible

4 What is the chance that you will get $100 at the weekend?

○ Certain ○ Likely
○ Unlikely ○ Impossible

5 Choose the impossible event.

○ You will be famous.
○ You will become rich.
○ A dog will bark.
○ A dog will grow wings and fly.

6 Choose the unlikely event.

○ You will smile next week.
○ You will read tomorrow.
○ A dog will come into the classroom.
○ A dog will chase a cat.

7 What is something that is likely to happen?

_____
_____
_____
_____
_____
_____

8 What is something that is unlikely to happen?

_____
_____
_____
_____
_____
_____

Name:

Class:

BLM 1

Hundreds, tens and ones chart

Hundreds	Tens	Ones

2

BLM 2

Number lines 0–20

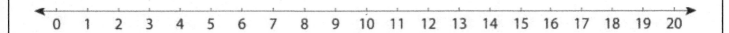

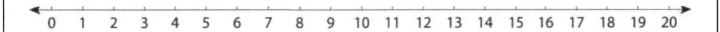

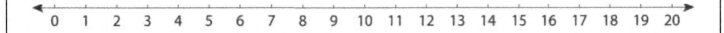

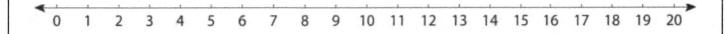

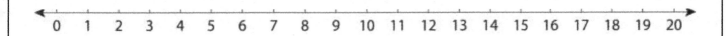

BLM 3

Subtraction think board

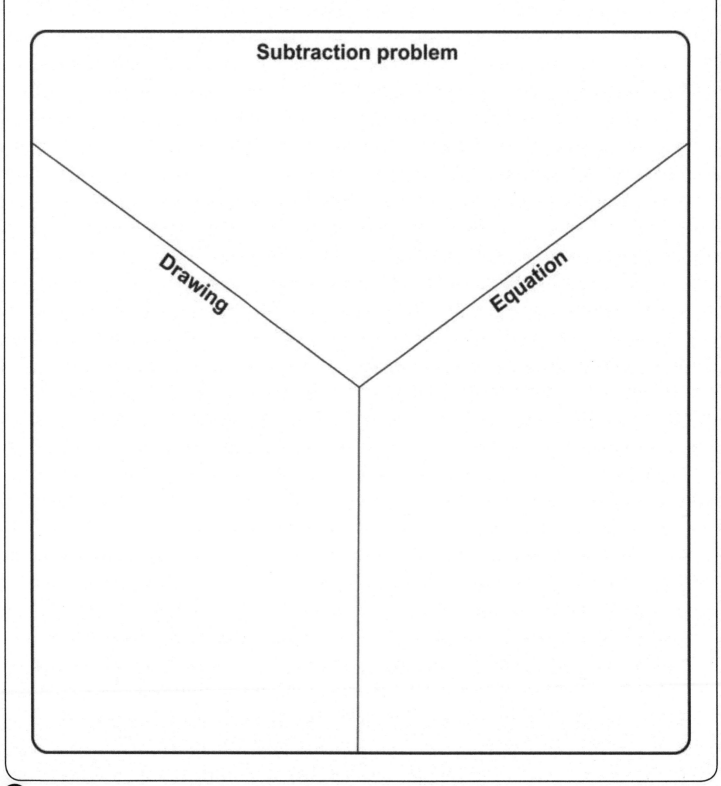

Subtraction problem

Drawing

Equation

BLM 4

Four in a row

Number board

8	23	6	12	2	17
33	4	21	28	42	10
16	20	18	19	5	1
14	25	39	26	22	3
13	30	9	7	11	23
35	29	12	15	24	27

Number cards

32	26	38	5	28	24
33	47	8	41	35	12
29	14	44	19	13	25

Name:

Class:

BLM 5

Array game board

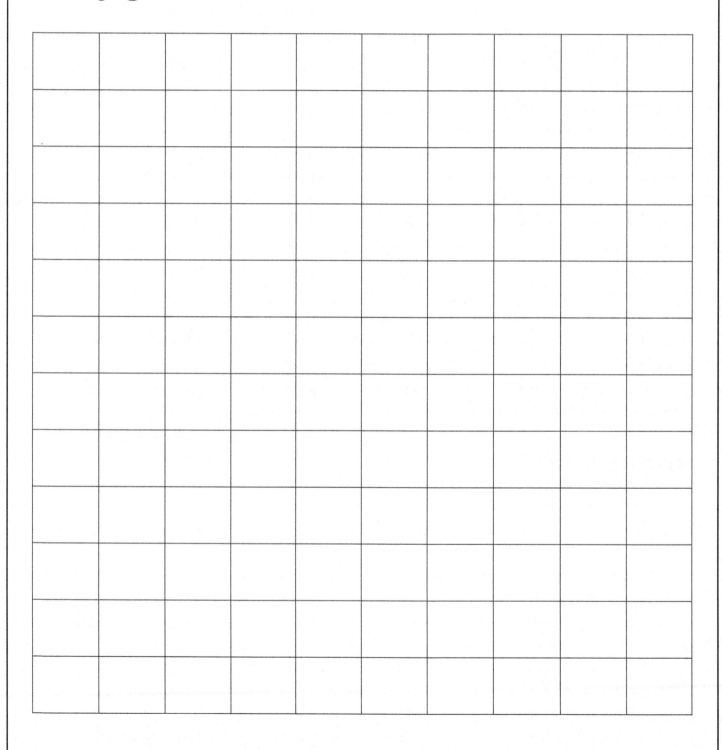

Name:

Class:

BLM 6

Party bag treats

Name:

Class:

BLM 7

Pizza topping fractions

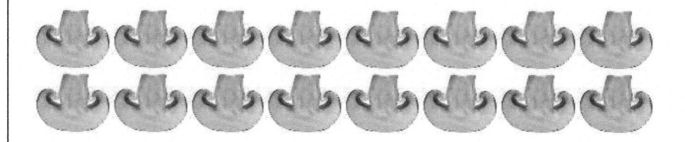

Name:

Class:

BLM 8

Grouping children

$\frac{1}{2}$	$\frac{1}{2}$		
$\frac{1}{4}$	$\frac{1}{4}$	$\frac{1}{4}$	$\frac{1}{4}$
$\frac{1}{8}$	$\frac{1}{8}$	$\frac{1}{8}$	$\frac{1}{8}$
$\frac{1}{8}$	$\frac{1}{8}$	$\frac{1}{8}$	$\frac{1}{8}$

Name:

Class:

BLM 9

10-frames

Name:

Class:

2

BLM 10

Hundred chart

1	2	3	4	5	6	7	8	9	10
11	12	13	14	15	16	17	18	19	20
21	22	23	24	25	26	27	28	29	30
31	32	33	34	35	36	37	38	39	40
41	42	43	44	45	46	47	48	49	50
51	52	53	54	55	56	57	58	59	60
61	62	63	64	65	66	67	68	69	70
71	72	73	74	75	76	77	78	79	80
81	82	83	84	85	86	87	88	89	90
91	92	93	94	95	96	97	98	99	100

Name:

Class:

BLM 11

Coin tracks

5c track
5c
10c
15c
20c
25c
30c
35c
40c
45c
50c

10c track
10c
20c
30c
40c
50c
60c
70c
80c
90c
$1

Name: _____

Class: _____

BLM 12

Pattern table

Number of students	Number of _____

Name:

Class:

2

BLM 13

Missing digit strips

Pattern 1
1, 3, 5, ___, 9, ___, 13, 15, ___, 19

Pattern 2
2, 5, 8, 11, ___, 17, ___, 23, ___

Pattern 3
60, ___, 50, 45, ___, 35, ___, 25, 20

Pattern 4
1, 2, 4, 8, ___, 32, 64, ___, ___

Pattern 5
1, 2, 4, 7, 11, ___, 22, ___, 37, ___

Pattern 6
2, 7, 6, 11, 10, ___, 14, 19, ___, ___

Pattern 7
100, 96, 92, ___, 88, 84, ___, 76, ___

Pattern 8
23, 33, ___, 53, 63, ___, 83, 93, ___

BLM 14

Think board

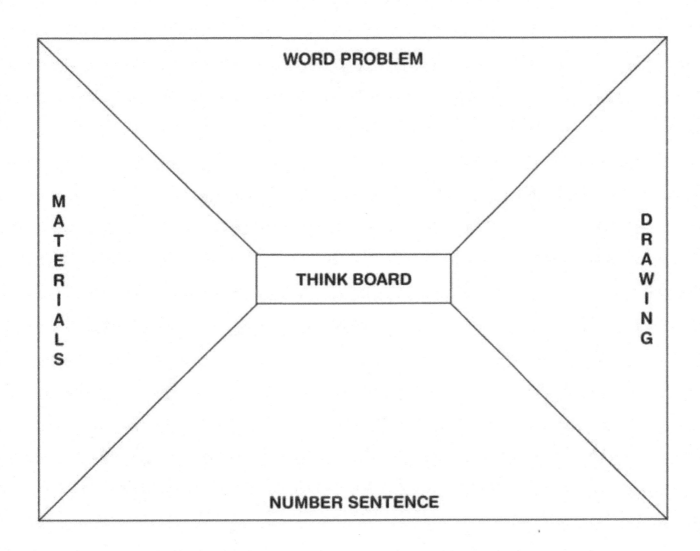

WORD PROBLEM

MATERIALS

THINK BOARD

DRAWING

NUMBER SENTENCE

Name:

Class:

BLM 15

Clock face and hands

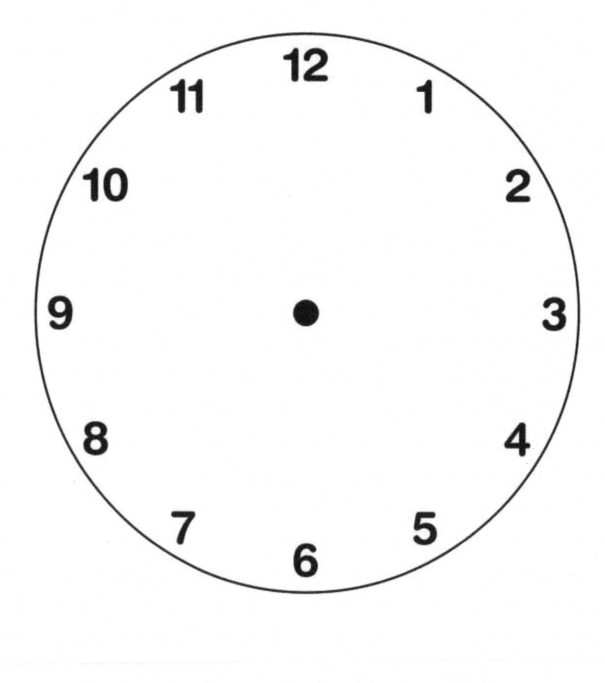

Oxford Mathematics Primary Years Programme Year 2 © Oxford University Press 2019. This sheet may be photocopied for non-commercial classroom use.

BLM 16

Months and seasons cards

April	August	December	spring
March	July	November	winter
February	June	October	autumn
January	May	September	summer

BLM 17

Calendar template

Month:

Name:

Class:

2

BLM 18

Alphabet template

A B C D E

F G H I J K

L M N O P

Q R S T U

V W X Y Z

Name:

Class:

BLM 19

Shape templates

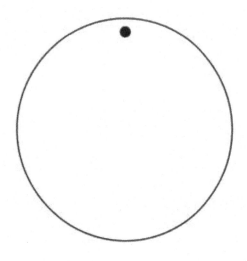
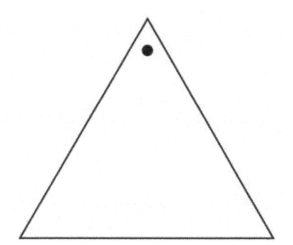
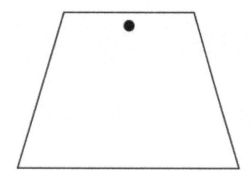
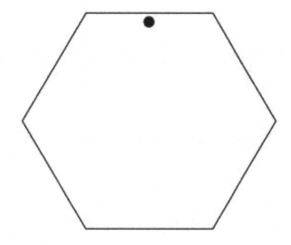

BLM 20

Probability cards

| impossible | certain |

| less likely | most likely |

| maybe |

Sunshine and rainfall

1 **a** As you know, there are 24 hours in a day. That means there are eight thousand, seven hundred and sixty hours in a year. Write the number using digits.

b Every day there is darkness and daylight. There are about forty-three hundred hours of daylight in a year. Write the number using digits.

2 This table shows the number of sunshine hours each year for some of the sunniest places in the world.

Place	Number of sunshine hours in a year
Upington, South Africa	3766
Phoenix, Arizona	4041
Atbara, Sudan	3739
Yuma, Arizona	4127
Aoulef, Algeria	3784

a Which place has the highest number of sunshine hours?

b Which places have fewer sunshine hours than Aoulef?

c Put the number of hours in order from lowest to highest.

d If Atbara had one more hour of sunshine each year, what would the number be?

(continued)

3 Rainfall is measured in millimetres. Match the clues to the numbers in the table to make a list of some of the wettest places in the world.

Place	Number of millimetres of rain in a year
	8636
	6502
	8989
	5451
	5916

Clues

- Quibdo, Colombia, has the highest rainfall in the list.

- The Bellenden Ker Range has the same digit in the thousands as Quibdo, Colombia.

- Henderson Lake, Canada, is almost halfway between 6000 and 7000.

- Dawei, Burma, has a 5 in the tens place.

- Kikori, Papua New Guinea, has a 9 in the hundreds place.

What do you think?

You will need

- a digital tablet (optional)

1 James, Georgia and Sadia have a total of 146 trading cards. How many cards might each of the three children have? Write five different number combinations that show this.

2 Four numbers are added to make 600. Write five different number combinations that might have been used.

3 What different ways could you add 86 and 88 in your head? Write as many answers as you can or record your thinking on a digital tablet.

Selling chocolates

Changing the order of numbers can make them easier to add. It's easier if you can get to the nearest 10.

For example, if you change the order of 17 + 38 + 23, you can add 17 and 23 first to get 40. Then it's easier to add 38.

The table shows how many chocolate bars five students sold for a school fundraiser.

Name	Week 1	Week 2	Week 3	Week 4	Best adding order	Total
Max	54	105	35	46		
Conroy	78	61	102	139		
Lottie	43	70	55	87		
Boneka	60	54	86	40		
Joey	36	82	91	62		

1 Choose the best order to add the numbers. Then find the totals.

2 Which student sold the most?

3 Which students sold the least?

Subtraction race

You will need

- two 6-sided dice

Find a partner. The first player rolls the dice and adds the two numbers that come up. The same player then subtracts the total from 100. Then the other player has a turn. (Write down the new total after each turn. On their next turn, the player then subtracts from their new number.)

Keep playing until one player reaches zero. The subtractions need to be done in your head.

When you finish, play again starting from 199 and subtracting down to 100, or use three dice to play from 199 down to zero.

Eating chocolate

The table lists the countries where the most chocolate bars are eaten each year. It shows how many 43 g chocolate bars are eaten per person in each of the countries.

Country	Chocolate bars (per person each year)
Switzerland	209
Germany	184
Austria	181
United Kingdom	174
Norway	153
Russia	123
Belgium	121
Australia	114

1 What is the difference in the number of chocolate bars eaten in Australia and Switzerland?

2 How many more chocolate bars are eaten in Germany than in Belgium?

3 The difference between the chocolate bars eaten in which two countries is exactly 58?

4 The difference between chocolate bars eaten in Austria and Australia is greater than the difference between chocolate bars eaten in Switzerland and Belgium. True or false?

Tim's Toyshop

When toys arrive at Tim's Toyshop, there are lots of things in each box. He needs to organise them.

1 There are 10 pencils in each jar. How many pencils are in these numbers of jars?

    a 3 jars   **b** 5 jars   **c** 8 jars   **d** 10 jars

2 The mini toy cars are in packs of two. How many cars are in these numbers of packs?

    a 8 packs   **b** 6 packs   **c** 10 packs   **d** 9 packs

3 There are 20 tennis balls in a box.

    a Tim makes packs of five. How many packs can he make?

    b If Tim changed his mind and made packs of four, how many packs could he make?

    c What other pack sizes could Tim make with an equal number of balls in each pack? Write number sentences to show how many pack sizes there could be.

    d If Tim makes packs of three, there would be some balls left over. How many packs of three could he make and how many balls would be left over?

Across the divide

You will need

- counters or other counting objects (optional)

There are lots of tricks to help you understand division and remember division facts. This activity will help you to think about division by particular numbers. You can use counters or other counting objects to check your answers.

1 For each of the numbers in the first column, write all the numbers from 1 to 30 that can be divided equally by that number. Then look at your list and record if the numbers are odd, even or both. The first one has been done for you.

Dividing by	Numbers that can be equally divided	Odd, even or both?
10	10, 20, 30	even
2		
3		
4		
5		
6		

2 Use the information from question 1 to answer true or false.

a If you divide a number by 10, the answer is always even.

b If you divide a number by 2, the answer is always odd.

c If you divide a number by 5, the answer might be odd or even.

d If you divide a number by 3, the answer might be odd or even.

e If you divide a number by 6, the answer is always even.

3 Write two interesting facts that you have learned about division. Share them with your class.

Computer patterns

Using Microsoft Word, or a similar computer program, is a quick and easy way to make fractions.

1 Follow the steps below to make fractions in Word.

   a Open a new Word document.

   b Choose **Table** from the **Insert** menu.

   c Make a table with four columns and two rows.

   d Highlight your table. In the **Layout** menu from the **Table Tools** tab, click on **Properties**.

   e Change the row height to 1 cm in the **Row** tab and the column width to 1 cm in the **Column** tab. Then click **OK**. You should now have a rectangle divided into eighths.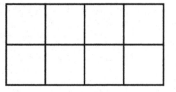

   f Select the top-left eighth of the rectangle.

   g In the **Design** menu from the **Table Tools** tab, click on **Shading** and pick a colour that you like. Your rectangle should now have one-eighth shaded.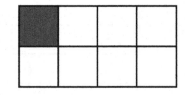

2 Use shading to make a fraction pattern in your shape.

3 Write a description that includes what fraction of the shape is in each colour.

4 Try making patterns in other shapes.

Fraction mystery

1 What was the butterfly's favourite school subject? Follow the fraction clues to find the letters in the answer and write them in order below.

a Write the letter that is the last $\frac{1}{4}$ of the word *them*.

b Write the letter that is the second $\frac{1}{2}$ of the word *to*.

c Write the letter that is the first $\frac{1}{8}$ of the word *thirteen*.

d Write the letter that is the second $\frac{1}{4}$ of the word *ship*.

e Write the letter that is the last $\frac{1}{6}$ of the word *circle*.

f Write the letter that is the first $\frac{1}{4}$ of the word *mine*.

g Write the letter that is the third fifth of the word *plate*.

h Write the letter that is the third quarter of the word *bite*.

i Write the letter that is the second eighth of the word *birthday*.

j Write the letter that is the second quarter of the word *aces*.

k Write the letter that is the last $\frac{1}{8}$ of the word *darkness*.

2 Make your own word fraction mystery with clues for a partner to solve.

International money

Many countries have dollars and cents as their form of money.

1 The United States of America has dollars and cents.

Which coin values does the United States of America have that your country also has? Which of their values are different?

2 New Zealand also has dollars and cents. Find out about New Zealand money and make a chart comparing their coins and notes with the coins and notes of the United States of America.

3 In Madagascar, there are five iraimbilanja in one ariary.

How many iraimbilanja are in the following?

a 10 ariary

b 20 ariary

c 30 ariary

d 200 ariary

e 100 ariary

f 1000 ariary

Money transactions

Some people save money for special events, such as going on holiday.

1 Tilly is saving money to spend on her family holiday. She puts $2.50 in her piggy bank every week for nine weeks.

    a Tilly could put a $2 coin and a 50c coin in her piggy bank each week. What are some other ways she could make $2.50?

    b How much is in her piggy bank after three weeks?

    c How much is in her piggy bank after nine weeks?

    d Tilly wants to save $40 for the holiday. What is the difference between the amount she has and the amount she wants?

2 Tilly's Auntie Amy gives her extra money. Now Tilly has $40. "Don't spend it all on one thing," her auntie says. Tilly divides the money up like this:

- $\frac{1}{8}$ to spend on snacks

- $\frac{1}{8}$ to spend on drinks

- $\frac{1}{4}$ to go to a show

- $\frac{1}{2}$ to have fun.

How much money will Tilly spend on each?

    a snacks   **b** drinks   **c** a show   **d** having fun

3 How many of each type of coin would Tilly need to make up $40?

    a $1 coins   **b** $2 coins   **c** 50c coins

(continued)

4 What ways could Tilly have $40 in notes?

5 On the way to the holiday, Tilly buys three ice-creams for her family.

    a Two ice-creams cost $2.20 each and one costs $2.45. How much does Tilly spend altogether?

    b She gives $7 to the ice-cream seller. There are six coins. What could they be?

    c Which coins could Tilly get as change?

6 On the last day, Tilly loses her purse. Her mother asks how much was in the purse. Tilly says there were three $2 coins, one $10 note, two 50c coins, four 20c coins and four 10c coins.

    a How much was in the purse?

    b Tilly's mother gives her half the amount. How much is that?

    c Tilly wants to use the money to go to a show. The ticket costs $10. How much more money does Tilly need?

    d Tilly's brother gives her the extra money. He also buys two ice-creams at the show for $1.75 each. How much money does Tilly's brother spend altogether?

7 If you had $50 to spend on your holiday, what would you use it for? Make a list of things you might buy. Then write a cost next to each thing on the list. Add them up to get a total cost.

Finding patterns

1 These marbles make a pattern.

   a Describe the way the pattern is made.

   b Copy the pattern and add the next five marbles.

2 Look at the pattern of 12 fish. The fish make a number pattern.

   a What number do you need to count by to find the smaller fish?

   b Would the 15th fish be bigger or smaller? How do you know?

   c Would the 24th fish be bigger or smaller? How do you know?

   d Draw the 36th fish.

3 There is a pattern in the way these teddy bears are drawn.

   a Describe the number order of the teddy bears with hats.

   b Describe the number order of the teddy bears holding the hearts.

   c Would the teddy at position 53 have a heart? How do you know?

   d Would the teddy at position 50 have a hat? How do you know?

   e Draw the teddy that would be at position 55.

   f Draw the teddy that would be at position 120.

4 **a** Draw a pattern of your own using shapes or objects.

   b Describe your patterns using numbers.

Computer problem solving

1 Sometimes you may need to investigate different ways to solve a problem. A computer can help save time.

Imagine that cup cakes are sold in packs of 5. We might want to know how many cup cakes are in 3 packs, 7 packs, 15 packs and so on. Below is a quick way to solve the problem using a computer.

- Open Microsoft Excel.
- Click in cell A1 and type *Packs*. Click in cell B1 and type *Cup cakes*.
- Click in cell A2 and type *2*.
- Now you're going to tell the computer that every pack has 5 cup cakes in it. You'll do this by telling it to multiply the number in A2 by 5. Click in cell B2. Type *= A2*5*. (The computer knows that * means "multiplied by".)
- Press **Enter** and *10* should appear in cell B2. (If it doesn't, ask your teacher or a classmate for help.)
- Now imagine there are 15 packs instead of 2 packs. Click on cell A2 again and type *15*. (There's no need to delete the 2. The computer will delete it for you.) Can you work out the number of cup cakes before the computer does?
- Press **Enter** and the computer will show the new total.

2 Try writing any number you like in cell A2. The computer will work out the answer as fast as you can press **Enter**!

3 Imagine there are 7 cup cakes in each pack. Change the number in cell B2 to multiply the packs by 7. Find the number of cup cakes in:

a 2 packs   **b** 6 packs   **c** 12 packs   **d** 18 packs.

Bedroom decorating

You will need

- grid paper

1 Allegra's room is 10 squares long and 6 squares wide.

a Draw the perimeter of Allegra's room on a piece of grid paper.

b What is the area of her room in squares?

2 Allegra needs to choose one of each of these for her room:

- a smaller bed that is 3 squares by 2 squares or a bigger bed that is 4 squares by 3 squares

- a smaller desk that is 3 squares by 1 square or a bigger desk that is 4 squares by 2 squares

- a chest of drawers that is 2 squares by 3 squares or a a chest of drawers that is 6 squares by 1 square.

a Choose one item from each point above. Then use your grid paper to show how they would fit in Allegra's room.

b What is the total area of the floor that is covered by the items?

3 Use grid paper to draw a plan of your ideal room.

a What is the total area of the room you have drawn?

b What area of the floor is covered?

Small dinosaurs

When we think of a dinosaur, we probably think of a huge animal. Some of them, like the diplodocus, were more than 30 metres long. But not all dinosaurs were huge. Skeletons of some very small dinosaurs have been found.

1 This table lists five of the smallest dinosaurs.

Name	Length
yandagornis	60 cm
bambiraptor	69 cm
microraptor	77 cm
micropachycephalosaurus	50 cm
saltopus	59 cm

a Rewrite the list showing the dinosaurs from shortest to longest.

b The shortest of all the dinosaurs has the longest dinosaur name: micropachycephalosaurus. If you write its name with 1 cm for each letter, how long would it be?

c Write micropachycephalosaurus in your normal handwriting. How long is the name in centimetres?

d What is the difference between the lengths of the longest and shortest dinosaurs on the list?

e If all five dinosaurs stood nose to tail, what would be the total length?

f What is the difference between your height and the length of the smallest dinosaur?

Make a container

You will need

- 12 blocks (or cubes)
- thin cardboard
- scissors
- glue or tape

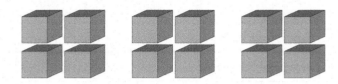

1 **a** Stack the blocks (or cubes) into at least two layers. Put the same number of blocks in each layer.

   b Now make a cardboard container that your blocks fit into exactly — in other words, a container with a volume of exactly 12 blocks.

2 **a** Find another way to stack the 12 blocks into equal layers. Will your new stack of blocks fit exactly into the container you made in question 1? Why or why not?

   b Make a container that your second stack of blocks fits into exactly.

3 Work out a way to compare the amount of cardboard you used for each container. Was it the same or different?

Heaviest and lightest animals

1 Here are some facts about heavy animals.

Animal fact	Animal	Mass
heaviest bird	ostrich	160 kg
heaviest rabbit	giant Flemish rabbit	5 kg
heaviest insect	goliath beetle	100 g
heaviest lizard	Komodo dragon	136 kg
heaviest dog	St Bernard	120 kg

a Which of the animals have a smaller mass than the Komodo dragon?

b What is the difference between the masses of the giant Flemish rabbit and the St Bernard?

c Does the goliath beetle have a mass of more or less than half a kilogram? How do you know?

d What is the mass of five St Bernards?

2 Here are some facts about light animals.

Animal fact	Animal	Mass
lightest dog	chihuahua	600 g
lightest rabbit	dwarf Dutch rabbit	500 g
lightest bird	hummingbird	3 g
lightest lizard	pygmy leaf chameleon	$\frac{1}{2}$ g
lightest monkey	pygmy marmoset	110 g

a Put the masses in order from lightest to heaviest.

b Which animals have a mass of half a kilogram or more?

c What is the difference between the masses of the hummingbird and the pygmy marmoset?

d How many dwarf Dutch rabbits would it take to balance a giant Flemish rabbit?

A day out

It was the day that Tilly and Billy had been waiting for. Mrs Williams was taking the class on an excursion to the wildlife park.

1 Tilly was excited. She woke up and looked at the clock.

   a What time did Tilly wake up?

   b Tilly's mother told her not to get up until 25 past 6. How much longer did she have to wait in bed?

   c Tilly closed her eyes but she could not go back to sleep. "I'll count to 60 and that will be a minute," she thought. Why did Tilly think that would be a minute?

   d Tilly counted to 60 a lot of times. "It must be 25 past 6 by now," she thought. Tilly looked at the clock again.

     What time was it when she looked at the clock the second time?

   e How many minutes had passed since the first time she looked?

2 Finally, it was 25 past 6. Tilly got up. Her brother Billy was already dressed. "I've been up for six minutes," he said.

   a What time did Billy get up?

   b It took Tilly two minutes to get dressed. How many seconds is that?

3 Tilly and Billy ate breakfast. They looked at the clock. "We have to be at school at quarter to 8 today," said Tilly. "That's just over half an hour from now."

   a What time do you think it was when Tilly said that?

(continued)

b It takes six minutes to walk to school. What time will they need to leave home?

c They looked at the clock again. Then Tilly and Billy went to clean their teeth. It took four minutes. What time did they finish cleaning their teeth?

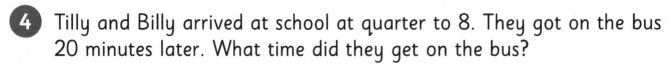

4 Tilly and Billy arrived at school at quarter to 8. They got on the bus 20 minutes later. What time did they get on the bus?

5 They arrived at the wildlife park at 18 minutes past 9. It took 10 minutes for everyone to go to the toilet. What time was it then?

6 Billy and his friend Lilly couldn't wait to see the kangaroos.

"We'll be seeing everything in good time," said Mrs Williams. "What time is it now?" she asked the students.

a What time was it?

b How long had it been since Tilly first woke up?

7 They went to see the kangaroos 20 minutes later. They fed them for a quarter of an hour.

a What time was it when they got to the kangaroos?

b How many minutes is a quarter of an hour?

c What time did they leave the kangaroos?

8 It was time to leave. Tilly and Billy got back to school at 5 past 2. Tilly fell asleep on the bus. How long had it been since she woke up in the morning?

9 Now write a short story about your day. Include the times for each main activity and draw clocks to show when things happened. Which of your activities lasted the longest? How long did it go for?

What season is it?

You will need

- an atlas (or the internet)

1 Use an atlas (or the internet) to find out whether each of the countries below is in the northern or the southern hemisphere.

Canada	France	Fiji	Egypt
India	Madagascar	Tonga	Japan
Nauru	United States of America		

2 Work out which season matches each country and month in this table.

Country	Month	Season
Madagascar	August	
United States of America	June	
India	December	
Japan	March	
Nauru	March	
France	January	
Egypt	October	

3 The Earth's tilt makes the southern hemisphere closer to the Sun in summer and further from the Sun in winter. It takes the Earth one year to travel around the Sun.

a Use the internet to find a diagram that shows the Earth's tilt during the different seasons. Then write a short explanation of why we have seasons.

b Why do you think the seasons are at different times of the year in the northern hemisphere and the southern hemisphere?

Day-of-year calendars

Most calendars divide the year into months and number the days in each month. But day-of-year calendars number the days in the whole year from 1 to 365 (or 366 in leap years).

This is a calendar showing the first four months of 2016 with the day-of-year numbers added (the bottom numbers).

JANUARY 2016

SUN	MON	TUE	WED	THU	FRI	SAT
					1	2
					1	2
3	4	5	6	7	8	9
3	4	5	6	7	8	9
10	11	12	13	14	15	16
10	11	12	13	14	15	16
17	18	19	20	21	22	23
17	18	19	20	21	22	23
24	25	26	27	28	29	30
24	25	26	27	28	29	30
31						
31						

FEBRUARY 2016

SUN	MON	TUE	WED	THU	FRI	SAT
	1	2	3	4	5	6
	32	33	34	35	36	37
7	8	9	10	11	12	13
38	39	40	41	42	43	44
14	15	16	17	18	19	20
45	46	47	48	49	50	51
21	22	23	24	25	26	27
52	53	54	55	56	57	58
28	29					
59	60					

MARCH 2016

SUN	MON	TUE	WED	THU	FRI	SAT
		1	2	3	4	5
		61	62	63	64	65
6	7	8	9	10	11	12
66	67	68	69	70	71	72
13	14	15	16	17	18	19
73	74	75	76	77	78	79
20	21	22	23	24	25	26
80	81	82	83	84	85	86
27	28	29	30	31		
87	88	89	90	91		

APRIL 2016

SUN	MON	TUE	WED	THU	FRI	SAT
					1	2
					92	93
3	4	5	6	7	8	9
94	95	96	97	98	99	100
10	11	12	13	14	15	16
101	102	103	104	105	106	107
17	18	19	20	21	22	23
108	109	110	111	112	113	114
24	25	26	27	28	29	30
115	116	117	118	119	120	121

1 Write the day of year for each of these dates.

   a 1 January   **b** 1 March   **c** 29 February

   d 20 January   **e** 17 March   **f** 30 April

2 How many days will be in the 2016 day-of-year calendar? How do you know?

3 What will be the days of year for these dates?

   a 1 May   **b** 31 December   **c** 25 December

4 Why are the day-of-year numbers for January the same as the dates?

5 Work out the day of year for your birthday.

(continued)

6 There are only two day-of-year calendars – one for normal years with 365 days and one for leap years. Fill in the table to show what day of year each calendar month starts and ends on.

Month	Normal year	Leap year
	Day number range	Day number range
January	1–31	1–31
February	32–59	
March		61–91
April		92–121
May	121–151	
June		
July	182–212	
August		214–244
September		245–274
October	274–304	
November		306–335
December		

7 Make your own day-of-year calendar for this year using the table on the next page. Start by filling in the year at the top.

a Number the days in January from 1 to 31 down the page.

b Number the days in February, starting at 32 and ending when you reach the date of 28 (or 29 if it is a leap year).

c Continue with the rest of the months. Remember to number the correct amount of days in each month. For example, there are 30 days in June and 31 days in July.

8 Use your calendar to find the day of year for the following.

a New Year's Day – 1 January

b Valentine's Day – 14 February

c Christmas Day – 25 December

(continued)

Day-of-year calendar for _____

Date	Jan	Feb	Mar	Apr	May	Jun	Jul	Aug	Sep	Oct	Nov	Dec
1												
2												
3												
4												
5												
6												
7												
8												
9												
10												
11												
12												
13												
14												
15												
16												
17												
18												
19												
20												
21												
22												
23												
24												
25												
26												
27												
28												
29												
30												
31												

Shape patterns

1. You can draw patterns and large shapes using 2D shapes on a computer. You can do this with a program like Microsoft Word.

   a   Open a new Word document.

   b   Click on **Shapes** from the **Insert** menu on the **Home** tab.

   c   Click on a square.

   d   Draw a square on the page.

   e   Copy the square.

   f   Paste four copies of the square so there is a total of five.

   g   Move the squares to make a pattern.

   h   Double click on each square and choose a colour to make a pattern.

2. Try out other shapes and patterns. Can you make a pattern with the following shapes that doesn't have any gaps?

   a   triangles   b   hexagons   c   rectangles   d   pentagons

3. You can put some shapes together to make other shapes. This parallelogram is made from one square and two triangles.

   a   Put two shapes together to make a new shape. Name the shapes you used and the shape you made.

   b   Repeat with three shapes and then four shapes.

Which object is that?

1 You can see 3D shapes everywhere you look. Think of a real-life object that matches each of the 3D shapes in the word bank. Try to draw a picture for each.

| triangular prism |
| sphere |
| rectangular prism |
| pyramid |
| cylinder |

2 You can see a 2D shape on each face of a 3D shape. For example, every face of a cube looks like this:

These are the faces of some 3D shapes. Name the shapes that they make.

Faces	3D shape
△ ▭ ▭ ▭ △	
▢ △ △ △ △	
▭ ▭ ▭ ▭ ▭ ▭	

3 We can compare pairs of shapes to find out what is similar and what is different. Record the name of each shape in the pairs and write what you find out in the table.

Pairs	Names	What is similar?	What is different?
	A sphere and a cylinder		

Treasure Island

1 The first thing you need to do when you get to Treasure Island is find the key to the treasure chest. It is behind one of the doors, but which one? Be careful – there are hidden dangers behind some of the doors. The dots are door handles and the squares are doors. Some doors are labelled. Follow the directions below and label the rest of the doors to show the dangers.

Find the key but ... BEWARE!

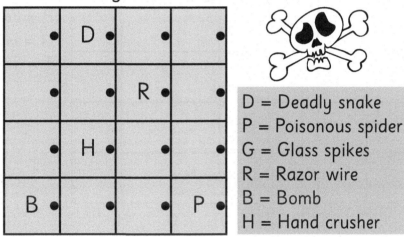

D = Deadly snake
P = Poisonous spider
G = Glass spikes
R = Razor wire
B = Bomb
H = Hand crusher

a There are glass spikes behind the top-left door.

b Poisonous spiders are asleep behind the top-right door. They are also behind the first and second doors on the second row from the top.

c There is a bomb behind the right door in the third row from the top.

d Deadly snakes are hidden behind the middle two doors in the bottom row.

e A hand crusher will spring out if you open the right-hand door in the second row from the top.

(continued)

f The first and third doors in the third row from the top have razor wire behind them.

g There is a bomb behind the third door in the top row.

h One of the bombs is fake. The key is behind *that* door. It is just below some razor wire and to the left of a deadly snake. Which door is the key behind?

2 Congratulations! You have the key. Now you must find the treasure chest. Here is a map of Treasure Island.

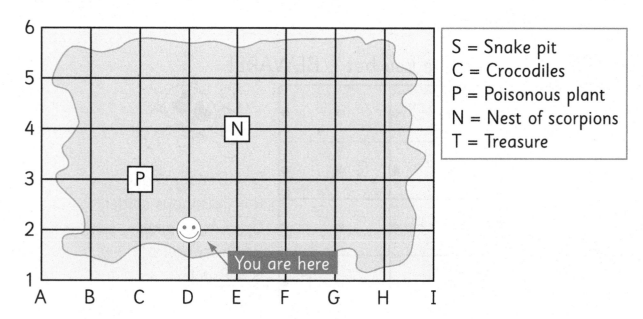

| S = Snake pit |
| C = Crocodiles |
| P = Poisonous plant |
| N = Nest of scorpions |
| T = Treasure |

To find your way, you must use the grid lines. Grid references describe the places where the grid lines join together. You are at D2 – this is where line D and line 2 join together.

a Which letter and number show the position of the nest of scorpions?

b Which letter and number show the position of the poisonous plant?

c There is a poisonous plant at B4, too. Put a letter P to show where it is.

d There is another nest of scorpions at G5. Put a letter N to show where it is.

(continued)

e There are crocodiles at C2 and E2. Mark them on the map.

f There are two snake pits — one is at D4 and the other is at G3. Mark them both on the map.

g The treasure chest is to the right of a poisonous plant and to the left of a snake pit. Put a letter T for "Treasure" at the correct point on the map.

h Which letter and number tell the position of the treasure?

3 You now need to find a way to the treasure from your starting point. Here are some rules:

- You can only follow the grid lines.
- You must not go over any dangerous locations.

a Write directions to get from D2 to the treasure. For example: Go forwards one square. Turn right. Go forwards …

b Draw a path to the treasure on your map. Congratulations! Use your key to open the treasure chest.

Sliding around

You will need

- grid paper

There are many ways to describe the way an object slides to move.

1 You could give the puppy on this grid these instructions to get to the bone.

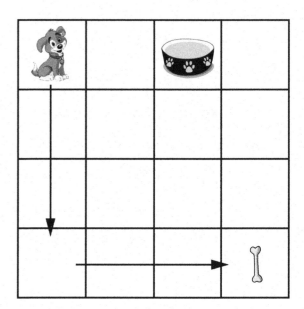

- Slide down three squares.
- Then slide right three squares.

a What has changed about the puppy? What has stayed the same?

b Write instructions to slide the puppy from the bone to the water bowl.

2 A slide can also move an object diagonally. Here's another way the puppy could be told to get to the bone.

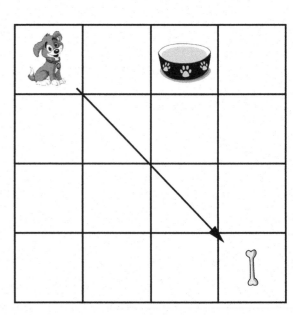

- Slide diagonally down and right three squares.

a Which way is faster?

b Write instructions to slide the puppy from the bone to the water bowl. Use at least one diagonal instruction.

(continued)

3 Follow the instructions to slide the pencil on the grid. Mark the movements as you go to make a letter of the alphabet.

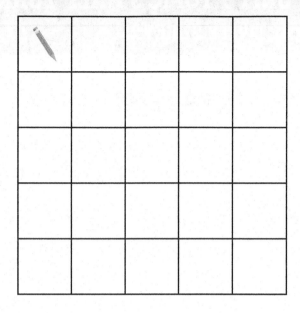

a Start at the tip of the pencil.

b Slide the pencil down three squares.

c Slide it right three squares.

d Slide it up one square.

e Slide it left two squares.

f Slide it up two squares.

g Slide it left one square.

4 Now it's your turn!

a Mark your own capital letter on the grid below.

b Write instructions to slide a pencil to make the letter.

c Swap with a partner and use grid paper to follow their instructions. Don't forget to draw the pencil in its start position for each other!

d Tell each other how well the instructions worked.

Amazing turns

You have to make lots of quarter turns to complete a maze. And sometimes if you go the wrong way, you need to make a half turn to go back again!

1 **a** Write instructions for how to finish the maze on the right, without drawing the path in.
Don't forget to say if your turns are clockwise or anticlockwise.

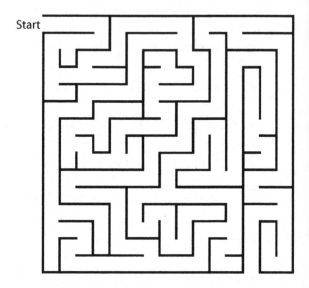

Start

b Swap with a partner and follow their instructions. Did you get to the end of the maze?

c Count how many quarter turns were needed to finish the maze.

2 **a** Draw your own maze. Make sure it includes quarter turns.

b Find a partner and have them do the maze while you watch. They need to describe the turns they make as they go along. Did they make any wrong turns or half turns to go back?

c Do the same for your partner, describing how to do their maze.

Popular names

1 This table shows the top 10 names for baby girls in 2010.

Position	Name	Tally marks	Number of letters
1st	Isabella		
2nd	Ruby		
3rd	Chloe		
4th	Olivia		
5th	Charlotte		
6th	Mia		
7th	Lily		
8th	Emily		
9th	Ella		
10th	Sienna		

a Use tally marks to count the number of letters in each name.

b Write in the total number of letters in each name.

c What is the longest name in each list? How many letters does it have?

d How many letters are in your name?

e What is the difference between the number of letters in your name and the longest name in the list?

2 **a** Make a list of the names of 10 students in your class.

b Make a tally of the number of letters in each of the 10 names.

c Write the number of letters in each name.

d What is the longest name? How many letters does it have?

e What is the shortest name? How many letters does it have?

f How do the longest names in 2010 compare with the longest names in your class list?

(continued)

3 This table shows the top 10 baby names for girls and boys in 2000.

Position	Girls	Boys
1st	Emily	Joshua
2nd	Jessica	Jack
3rd	Olivia	Lachlan
4th	Sarah	James
5th	Chloe	Thomas
6th	Georgia	Matthew
7th	Emma	Daniel
8th	Hannah	Nicholas
9th	Isabella	Benjamin
10th	Stephanie	William

You will be conducting a **survey** to find out what students in your class think about these names. In a survey, you get information from people.

a Is it best to ask girls about girls' names and boys about boys' names? Write a reason for your answer.

b If you only asked one person, you would not get a fair idea of the favourite name. How many people do you think you should ask? Write a reason for your answer.

c Write a survey question to find out which is the favourite name on the list among your classmates.

d Conduct the survey and record the results.

Keeping track of information

1 You can use a tally to make a **frequency table**. If you look at these number words, you can see that some have more letters than others.

> one two three four five six seven eight nine ten eleven twelve
> thirteen fourteen fifteen sixteen seventeen eighteen nineteen twenty

a Make a frequency table showing the number of letters in the words above. Count how many letters are in each word and make a tally to show how many words have three letters, four letters and so on. Then write the total for each column.

Number of letters in word	3	4	5	6	7	8	9
Tally	||||						
Total							

b How many of the number words have three letters?

c Which number word has the most letters?

d How many of the other words have the same number of letters as the word *eight*?

2 Find out some information about the students in your classroom. Use the information to make a frequency table. For example, you could watch to see how many students are out of their seats, talking or working hard.

Mark what happens in the frequency table every two minutes for 10 minutes.

(continued)

3 When people make up a survey question, sometimes they think they know how people will answer.

a Write a survey question that you think most people in your class would answer "yes" to.

b Would you get the same answers if you asked students in Year 6? Why or why not?

c Do you think the answers would change if adults were asked the same question?

4 **a** Think of a survey question that you think would make half the class answer "yes" and half answer "no".

	Tally	Total
Yes	卌 卌	10
No	卌 卌	10

b Try your survey on 20 students.

c Make a tally of the results.

d Were the results what you expected? Why or why not?

5 **a** Choose another survey question — one that you *don't* know how students will answer. It could be something about favourite TV shows or the number of pets students have.

b Write your survey question and draw a frequency table to record the results in.

c Decide how many students in the class you will ask.

d Carry out the survey. Tally and total your results.

e Write two sentences about what you found out.

The world's tallest

1 This table shows the countries that had the top 10 tallest buildings in the world in 2014. It also shows the height of these buildings.

Country	Height
United Arab Emirates	828 metres
Saudi Arabia	595 metres
USA	541 metres
Taiwan	509 metres
China	492 metres
Hong Kong	483 metres
Malaysia	452 metres
China	450 metres
USA	442 metres
China	440 metres

a Where was the building that was 440 metres tall?

b How many of the top 10 tall buildings were in China?

c In which country was the building exactly 40 metres taller than the one in Malaysia?

d Which country had two buildings in the list?

(continued)

2 The countries from the 2014 list are represented in this pictograph.

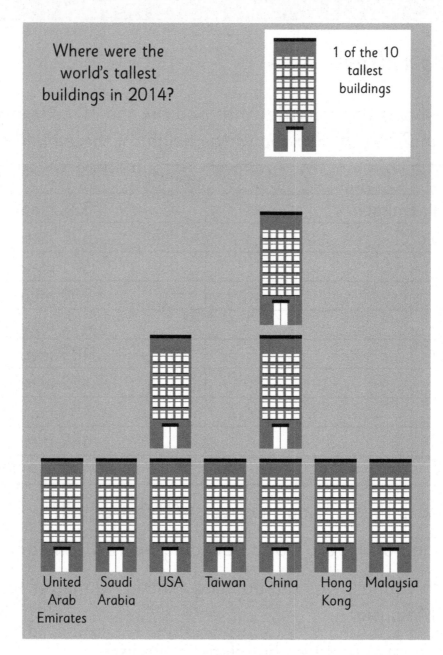

a How many of the tallest buildings were in Malaysia?

b Which country had the greatest number of buildings in the top 10 tallest list?

c What was the difference between the number of buildings in China and the USA?

d What information about the tallest buildings is in the table but *not* in the pictograph?

(continued)

3 The world's tallest bridge is in France. This list shows the countries that have the top 10 tallest bridges in the world. It also shows the number of these bridges in each country.

France: 1	Russia: 1	China: 4	Japan: 1	South Korea: 1	Hong Kong: 1	Denmark: 1

Make a pictograph like the one in question 2 showing where the world's tallest bridges are.

4 Use Microsoft Excel to make a bar graph about the tallest bridges.

   a Open a new Excel document.

   b Click on cell A1 and type *France*.

   c Click on cell B1 and type *1*.

   d Click on cell A2 and type *Russia*.

   e Click on cell B2 and type *1*.

   f Continue adding the rest of the data.

   g Hold the **Shift** key, click on cell A1 and then click on cell B7 (this will highlight all the information for your graph).

   h From the menu bar at the top of the page, choose **Charts** and then select **Column**. Choose the **Clustered column** option and a bar graph will appear on the page.

5 Try some of the other graph types on the **Charts** menu. Choose your favourite to print out, or save the graph and share it with your classmates.

6 Do some research on the world's tallest people.

   a Make a graph. You can choose which sort of graph.

   b Type the information into Excel and make a different kind of graph.

   c Write five things about the information that you found.

What's on for the weekend?

Evie and Taj were talking about what they planned to do on the weekend. Taj likes to paint but he's not interested in sport at all. Evie loves netball. She likes art but it's not her favourite thing to do.

1 Evie told Taj that there was something she would definitely be doing on the weekend. What might that be? List three things.

2 Evie asked Taj if he was going to do a particular thing on the weekend. Taj said it was unlikely. What might Evie have asked about? List three things.

3 Do you think Evie or Taj is more likely to do each of these things on the weekend? Or do you think the chance is equal? Give a reason for each answer.

a Go shopping **b** Go running

c Go to a cartooning workshop **d** Eat pizza

4 Choose a word from the table to describe the chance of each event.

possible
impossible
certain
likely
unlikely
equal chance
might

a Evie playing netball on the weekend.

b Taj playing netball on the weekend.

c Evie painting on the weekend.

d Evie and Taj seeing a movie together on the weekend.

e Evie and Taj travelling interstate on the weekend.

f Evie and Taj travelling to the Sun on the weekend.

g Taj sleeping on the weekend.

PRE- AND POST-ASSESSMENT TEST ANSWERS

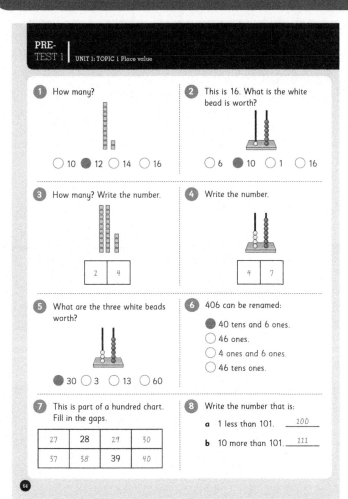

1 How many?

○ 10 ● 12 ○ 14 ○ 16

2 This is 16. What is the white bead is worth?

○ 6 ● 10 ○ 1 ○ 16

3 How many? Write the number.

2 4

4 Write the number.

4 7

5 What are the three white beads worth?

● 30 ○ 3 ○ 13 ○ 60

6 406 can be renamed:

● 40 tens and 6 ones.
○ 46 ones.
○ 4 ones and 6 ones.
○ 46 tens ones.

7 This is part of a hundred chart. Fill in the gaps.

27	28	29	30
37	38	39	40

8 Write the number that is:

a 1 less than 101. ___100___

b 10 more than 101. ___111___

64

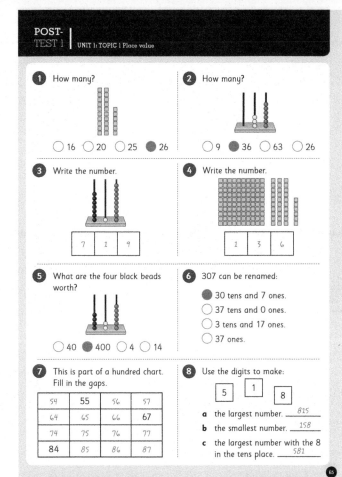

1 How many?

○ 16 ○ 20 ○ 25 ● 26

2 How many?

○ 9 ● 36 ○ 63 ○ 26

3 Write the number.

7 1 9

4 Write the number.

1 3 6

5 What are the four black beads worth?

○ 40 ● 400 ○ 4 ○ 14

6 307 can be renamed:

● 30 tens and 7 ones.
○ 37 tens and 0 ones.
○ 3 tens and 17 ones.
○ 37 ones.

7 This is part of a hundred chart. Fill in the gaps.

54	55	56	57
64	65	66	67
74	75	76	77
84	85	86	87

8 Use the digits to make:

5 1 8

a the largest number. ___815___

b the smallest number. ___158___

c the largest number with the 8 in the tens place. ___581___

65

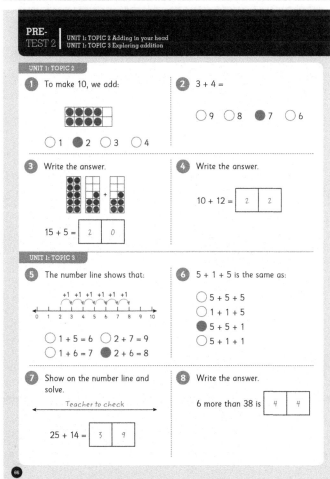

UNIT 1: TOPIC 2

1 To make 10, we add:

○ 1 ● 2 ○ 3 ○ 4

2 3 + 4 =

○ 9 ○ 8 ● 7 ○ 6

3 Write the answer.

15 + 5 = 2 0

4 Write the answer.

10 + 12 = 2 2

UNIT 1: TOPIC 3

5 The number line shows that:

○ 1 + 5 = 6 ○ 2 + 7 = 9
○ 1 + 6 = 7 ● 2 + 6 = 8

6 5 + 1 + 5 is the same as:

○ 5 + 5 + 5
○ 1 + 1 + 5
● 5 + 5 + 1
○ 5 + 1 + 1

7 Show on the number line and solve.

Teacher to check

25 + 14 = 3 9

8 Write the answer.

6 more than 38 is 4 4

66

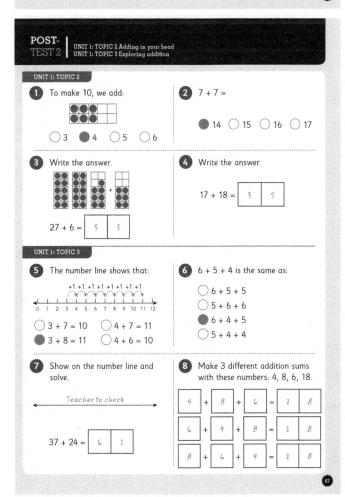

UNIT 1: TOPIC 2

1 To make 10, we add:

○ 3 ● 4 ○ 5 ○ 6

2 7 + 7 =

● 14 ○ 15 ○ 16 ○ 17

3 Write the answer.

27 + 6 = 3 3

4 Write the answer.

17 + 18 = 3 5

UNIT 1: TOPIC 3

5 The number line shows that:

○ 3 + 7 = 10 ○ 4 + 7 = 11
● 3 + 8 = 11 ○ 4 + 6 = 10

6 6 + 5 + 4 is the same as:

○ 6 + 5 + 5
○ 5 + 6 + 6
● 6 + 4 + 5
○ 5 + 4 + 4

7 Show on the number line and solve.

Teacher to check

37 + 24 = 6 1

8 Make 3 different addition sums with these numbers: 4, 8, 6, 18.

4 + 8 + 6 = 1 8

6 + 4 + 8 = 1 8

8 + 6 + 4 = 1 8

67

PRE- AND POST-ASSESSMENT TEST ANSWERS

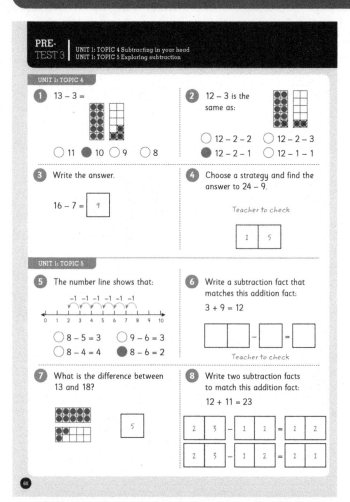

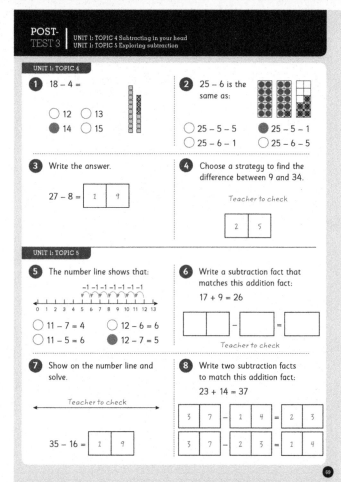

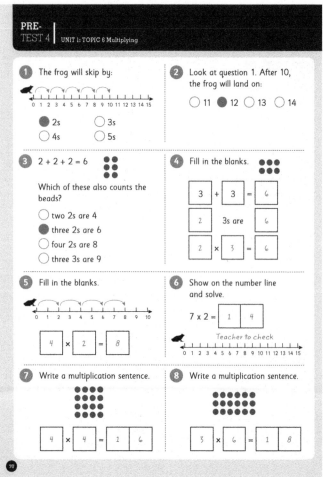

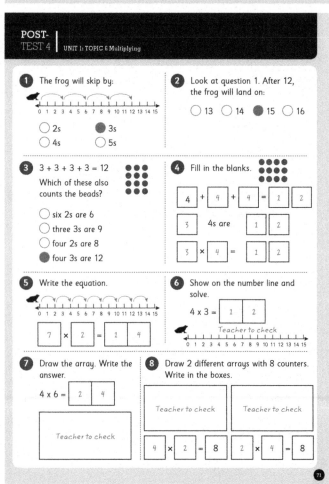

OXFORD UNIVERSITY PRESS

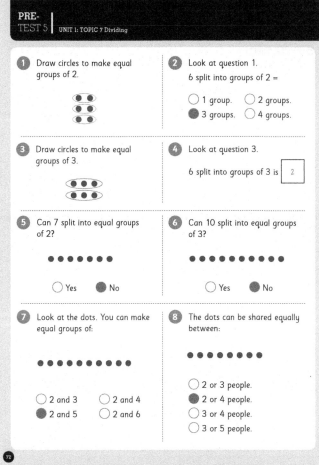

1. Draw circles to make equal groups of 2.

2. Look at question 1.
   6 split into groups of 2 =
   - ○ 1 group.
   - ○ 2 groups.
   - ● 3 groups.
   - ○ 4 groups.

3. Draw circles to make equal groups of 3.

4. Look at question 3.
   6 split into groups of 3 is [2]

5. Can 7 split into equal groups of 2?
   - ○ Yes
   - ● No

6. Can 10 split into equal groups of 3?
   - ○ Yes
   - ● No

7. Look at the dots. You can make equal groups of:
   - ○ 2 and 3
   - ○ 2 and 4
   - ● 2 and 5
   - ○ 2 and 6

8. The dots can be shared equally between:
   - ● 2 or 4 people.
   - ○ 2 or 3 people.
   - ○ 3 or 4 people.
   - ○ 3 or 5 people.

72

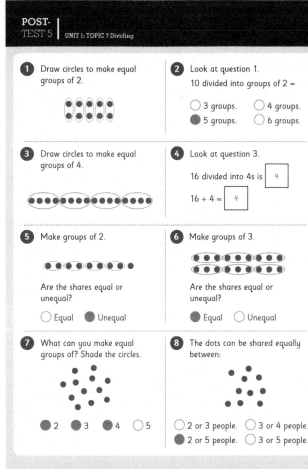

1. Draw circles to make equal groups of 2.

2. Look at question 1.
   10 divided into groups of 2 =
   - ○ 3 groups.
   - ○ 4 groups.
   - ● 5 groups.
   - ○ 6 groups.

3. Draw circles to make equal groups of 4.

4. Look at question 3.
   16 divided into 4s is [4]
   $16 \div 4 =$ [4]

5. Make groups of 2.
   Are the shares equal or unequal?
   - ○ Equal
   - ● Unequal

6. Make groups of 3.
   Are the shares equal or unequal?
   - ● Equal
   - ○ Unequal

7. What can you make equal groups of? Shade the circles.
   - ● 2
   - ● 3
   - ● 4
   - ○ 5

8. The dots can be shared equally between:
   - ○ 2 or 3 people.
   - ○ 3 or 4 people.
   - ● 2 or 5 people.
   - ○ 3 or 5 people.

73

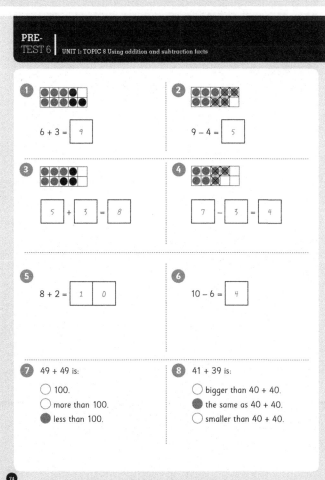

1. $6 + 3 =$ [9]

2. $9 - 4 =$ [5]

3. [5] + [3] = [8]

4. [7] - [3] = [4]

5. $8 + 2 =$ [1 | 0]

6. $10 - 6 =$ [4]

7. 49 + 49 is:
   - ○ 100.
   - ○ more than 100.
   - ● less than 100.

8. 41 + 39 is:
   - ○ bigger than 40 + 40.
   - ● the same as 40 + 40.
   - ○ smaller than 40 + 40.

74

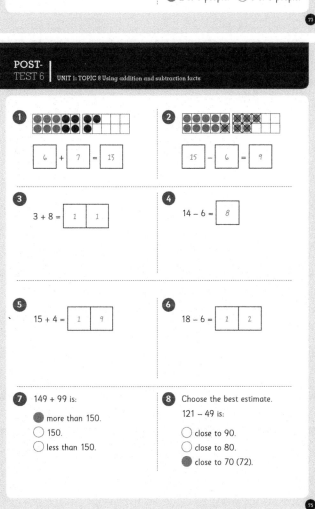

1. [6] + [7] = [13]

2. [15] - [6] = [9]

3. $3 + 8 =$ [1 | 1]

4. $14 - 6 =$ [8]

5. $15 + 4 =$ [1 | 9]

6. $18 - 6 =$ [1 | 2]

7. 149 + 99 is:
   - ● more than 150.
   - ○ 150.
   - ○ less than 150.

8. Choose the best estimate.
   121 – 49 is:
   - ○ close to 90.
   - ○ close to 80.
   - ● close to 70 (72).

75

PRE- AND POST-ASSESSMENT TEST ANSWERS

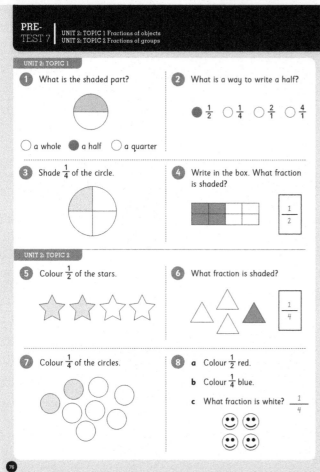

UNIT 2: TOPIC 1

1. What is the shaded part?
   ○ a whole ● a half ○ a quarter

2. What is a way to write a half?
   ● $\frac{1}{2}$ ○ $\frac{1}{4}$ ○ $\frac{2}{1}$ ○ $\frac{4}{1}$

3. Shade $\frac{1}{4}$ of the circle.

4. Write in the box. What fraction is shaded?
   $\frac{1}{2}$

UNIT 2: TOPIC 2

5. Colour $\frac{1}{2}$ of the stars.

6. What fraction is shaded?
   $\frac{1}{4}$

7. Colour $\frac{1}{4}$ of the circles.

8. a Colour $\frac{1}{2}$ red.
   b Colour $\frac{1}{4}$ blue.
   c What fraction is white? $\frac{1}{4}$

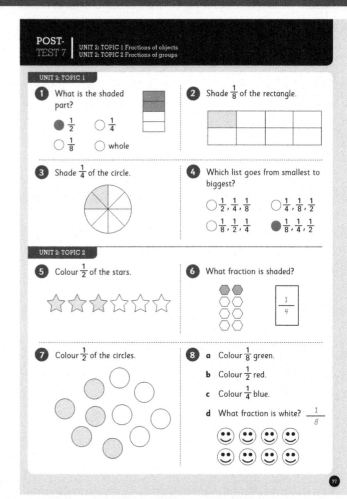

UNIT 2: TOPIC 1

1. What is the shaded part?
   ● $\frac{1}{2}$ ○ $\frac{1}{4}$
   ○ $\frac{1}{8}$ ○ whole

2. Shade $\frac{1}{8}$ of the rectangle.

3. Shade $\frac{1}{4}$ of the circle.

4. Which list goes from smallest to biggest?
   ○ $\frac{1}{2}, \frac{1}{4}, \frac{1}{8}$ ○ $\frac{1}{4}, \frac{1}{8}, \frac{1}{2}$
   ○ $\frac{1}{8}, \frac{1}{2}, \frac{1}{4}$ ● $\frac{1}{8}, \frac{1}{4}, \frac{1}{2}$

UNIT 2: TOPIC 2

5. Colour $\frac{1}{2}$ of the stars.

6. What fraction is shaded?
   $\frac{1}{4}$

7. Colour $\frac{1}{2}$ of the circles.

8. a Colour $\frac{1}{8}$ green.
   b Colour $\frac{1}{2}$ red.
   c Colour $\frac{1}{4}$ blue.
   d What fraction is white? $\frac{1}{8}$

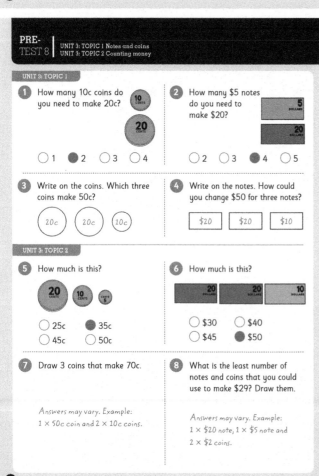

UNIT 3: TOPIC 1

1. How many 10c coins do you need to make 20c?
   ○ 1 ● 2 ○ 3 ○ 4

2. How many $5 notes do you need to make $20?
   ○ 2 ○ 3 ● 4 ○ 5

3. Write on the coins. Which three coins make 50c?
   20c 20c 10c

4. Write on the notes. How could you change $50 for three notes?
   $20 $20 $10

UNIT 3: TOPIC 2

5. How much is this?
   ○ 25c ● 35c
   ○ 45c ○ 50c

6. How much is this?
   ○ $30 ○ $40
   ○ $45 ● $50

7. Draw 3 coins that make 70c.
   Answers may vary. Example:
   1 × 50c coin and 2 × 10c coins.

8. What is the least number of notes and coins that you could use to make $29? Draw them.
   Answers may vary. Example:
   1 × $20 note, 1 × $5 note and 2 × $2 coins.

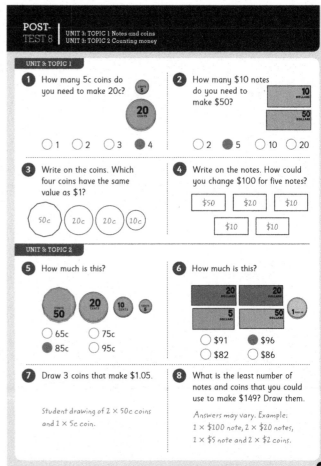

UNIT 3: TOPIC 1

1. How many 5c coins do you need to make 20c?
   ○ 1 ○ 2 ○ 3 ● 4

2. How many $10 notes do you need to make $50?
   ○ 2 ● 5 ○ 10 ○ 20

3. Write on the coins. Which four coins have the same value as $1?
   50c 20c 20c 10c

4. Write on the notes. How could you change $100 for five notes?
   $50 $20 $10
   $10 $10

UNIT 3: TOPIC 2

5. How much is this?
   ○ 65c ○ 75c
   ● 85c ○ 95c

6. How much is this?
   ○ $91 ● $96
   ○ $82 ○ $86

7. Draw 3 coins that make $1.05.
   Student drawing of 2 × 50c coins and 1 × 5c coin.

8. What is the least number of notes and coins that you could use to make $149? Draw them.
   Answers may vary. Example:
   1 × $100 note, 2 × $20 notes, 1 × $5 note and 2 × $2 coins.

OXFORD UNIVERSITY PRESS

UNIT 4: TOPIC 1

1 What is the missing number?

| 0 | 2 | 4 | | 8 | 10 |

○ 4 ○ 5 ● 6 ○ 7

2 How many do the numbers go down by?

| 20 | 18 | 16 | 14 | 12 | 10 |

○ 1 ● 2 ○ 3 ○ 4

3 What is the next number in the pattern?

0 1 2 3 4 5 6 7 8 9 10 11 12 13

○ 10 ○ 11 ● 12 ○ 13

4 If the numbers in a pattern end in 5, then 0, then 5, then 0, then 5, then 0, you would be counting by:

○ 2 ○ 3 ○ 4 ● 5

UNIT 4: TOPIC 2

5 Sam has 2 toys. He gets 1 more. Which number sentence matches the story?

○ 2 + 2 = 4   ● 2 + 1 = 3
○ 2 − 2 = 0   ○ 2 − 1 = 1

6 Write a number sentence for this story. Emma has 3 toys. She loses 2.

| 3 | − | 2 | = | 1 |

7 Jack has $10. He spends $3. How much does he have left?

_____ $7 _____

Is this addition or subtraction?

○ Addition ● Subtraction

8 Lucy has 9 marbles. She loses 3. How many does she have left? Write a number sentence to show the answer.

_____ 9 − 3 = 6 _____

80

POST-
TEST 9 | UNIT 5: TOPIC 1 Length and area
UNIT 5: TOPIC 2 Metres and centimetres

UNIT 4: TOPIC 1

1 Fill in the blanks in this counting pattern.

| 0 | 2 | 4 | 6 | 8 | 10 | 12 | 14 |

2 The numbers go down by:

| 30 | 27 | 24 | 21 | 18 | 15 | 12 | 9 |

○ 2 ● 3 ○ 4 ○ 5

3 Fill in the blanks for this pattern.

| 2 | 6 | 10 | 14 | 18 | 22 | 26 | 30 |

4 If the last digit in a pattern was:
3, 8, 3, 8, 3, 8
you would be counting by:

○ 2 ○ 3 ○ 4 ● 5

UNIT 4: TOPIC 2

5 Sam has 7 toys. He loses 2. Which number sentence matches the story?

○ 7 + 2 = 9
○ 7 + 3 = 10
● 7 − 2 = 5
○ 7 − 7 = 0

6 Tom has 5 cars. He gets 4 more. Write a number sentence for the story.

| 5 | + | 4 | = | 9 |

7 Eva has $25. She spends $13. How much does she have left?

_____ $12 _____

Did you add or subtract?

○ Added ● Subtracted

8 Tran reads 11 pages at school. He reads 8 pages at home. How many pages does he read altogether? Write a number sentence to show the answer.

_____ 11 + 8 = 19 _____

81

PRE-
TEST 10 | UNIT 5: TOPIC 1 Length and area
UNIT 5: TOPIC 2 Metres and centimetres

UNIT 5: TOPIC 1

1 How many hand spans long is the line?

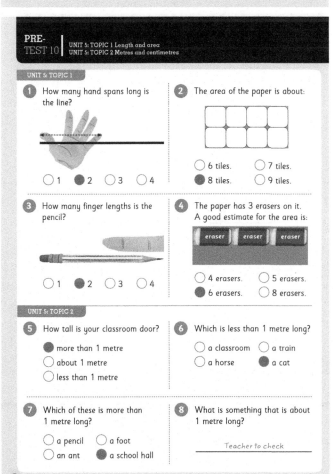

○ 1 ● 2 ○ 3 ○ 4

2 The area of the paper is about:

○ 6 tiles.   ○ 7 tiles.
● 8 tiles.   ○ 9 tiles.

3 How many finger lengths is the pencil?

○ 1 ● 2 ○ 3 ○ 4

4 The paper has 3 erasers on it. A good estimate for the area is:

eraser eraser eraser

○ 4 erasers.   ○ 5 erasers.
● 6 erasers.   ○ 8 erasers.

UNIT 5: TOPIC 2

5 How tall is your classroom door?

● more than 1 metre
○ about 1 metre
○ less than 1 metre

6 Which is less than 1 metre long?

○ a classroom ○ a train
○ a horse   ● a cat

7 Which of these is more than 1 metre long?

○ a pencil ○ a foot
○ an ant   ● a school hall

8 What is something that is about 1 metre long?

_____ Teacher to check _____

82

POST-
TEST 10 | UNIT 5: TOPIC 1 Length and area
UNIT 5: TOPIC 2 Metres and centimetres

UNIT 5: TOPIC 1

1 How many fingers long is the line?

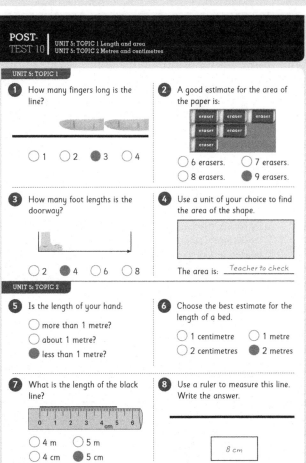

○ 1 ○ 2 ● 3 ○ 4

2 A good estimate for the area of the paper is:

eraser eraser eraser
eraser eraser
eraser

○ 6 erasers.   ○ 7 erasers.
○ 8 erasers.   ● 9 erasers.

3 How many foot lengths is the doorway?

○ 2 ● 4 ○ 6 ○ 8

4 Use a unit of your choice to find the area of the shape.

The area is: _____ Teacher to check _____

UNIT 5: TOPIC 2

5 Is the length of your hand:

○ more than 1 metre?
○ about 1 metre?
● less than 1 metre?

6 Choose the best estimate for the length of a bed.

○ 1 centimetre   ○ 1 metre
○ 2 centimetres   ● 2 metres

7 What is the length of the black line?

○ 4 m   ○ 5 m
○ 4 cm ● 5 cm

8 Use a ruler to measure this line. Write the answer.

8 cm

83

PRE- AND POST-ASSESSMENT TEST ANSWERS

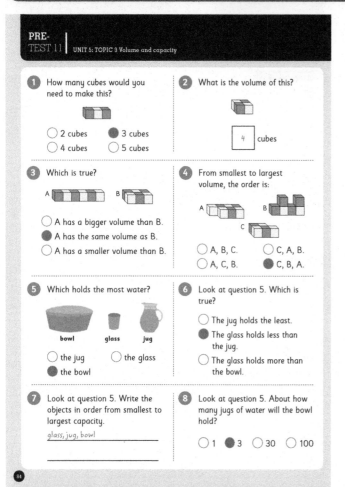

1. How many cubes would you need to make this?
   - ○ 2 cubes
   - ● 3 cubes
   - ○ 4 cubes
   - ○ 5 cubes

2. What is the volume of this?
   - [4] cubes

3. Which is true?
   A   B
   - ○ A has a bigger volume than B.
   - ● A has the same volume as B.
   - ○ A has a smaller volume than B.

4. From smallest to largest volume, the order is:
   A   B   C
   - ○ A, B, C.
   - ○ C, A, B.
   - ○ A, C, B.
   - ● C, B, A.

5. Which holds the most water?
   bowl   glass   jug
   - ○ the jug
   - ○ the glass
   - ● the bowl

6. Look at question 5. Which is true?
   - ○ The jug holds the least.
   - ● The glass holds less than the jug.
   - ○ The glass holds more than the bowl.

7. Look at question 5. Write the objects in order from smallest to largest capacity.
   glass, jug, bowl

8. Look at question 5. About how many jugs of water will the bowl hold?
   - ○ 1   ● 3   ○ 30   ○ 100

84

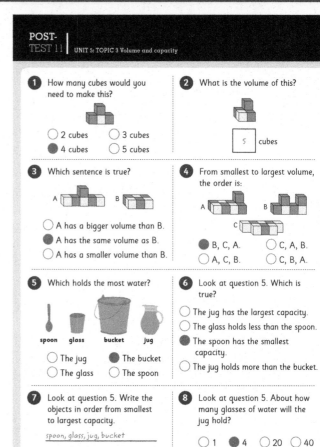

1. How many cubes would you need to make this?
   - ○ 2 cubes
   - ○ 3 cubes
   - ● 4 cubes
   - ○ 5 cubes

2. What is the volume of this?
   - [5] cubes

3. Which sentence is true?
   A   B
   - ○ A has a bigger volume than B.
   - ● A has the same volume as B.
   - ○ A has a smaller volume than B.

4. From smallest to largest volume, the order is:
   A   B   C
   - ● B, C, A.
   - ○ C, A, B.
   - ○ A, C, B.
   - ○ C, B, A.

5. Which holds the most water?
   spoon   glass   bucket   jug
   - ○ The jug
   - ● The bucket
   - ○ The glass
   - ○ The spoon

6. Look at question 5. Which is true?
   - ○ The jug has the largest capacity.
   - ○ The glass holds less than the spoon.
   - ● The spoon has the smallest capacity.
   - ○ The jug holds more than the bucket.

7. Look at question 5. Write the objects in order from smallest to largest capacity.
   spoon, glass, jug, bucket

8. Look at question 5. About how many glasses of water will the jug hold?
   - ○ 1   ● 4   ○ 20   ○ 40

85

1. The mouse is:
   - ○ heavier.
   - ● lighter.

2. The mouse is:
   - ● heavier.
   - ○ lighter.

3. Which is true?
   - ○ The pencil is heavier.
   - ○ The sharpener is heavier.
   - ● They balance each other.

4. Draw a red ball at one end of the scale and a white ball at the other to show that the red ball is heavier.
   Student drawing of red ball at lower end and white ball at higher end

5. Draw something that is heavier than the pencil.
   Teacher to check

6. Draw something that is lighter than the pencil.
   Teacher to check

7. Which would have about the same mass as you?
   - ○ a cat
   - ○ a horse
   - ● a big dog
   - ○ a mouse

8. Write the labels of the objects (A, B and C) in order from lightest to heaviest.
   A   B   C
   A C B

86

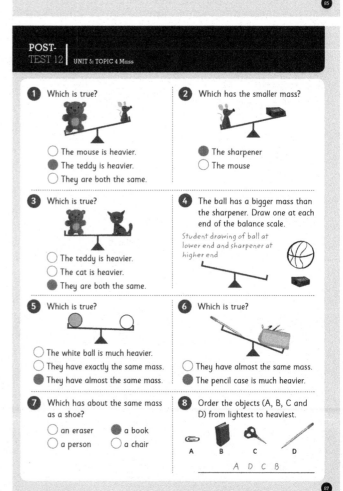

1. Which is true?
   - ○ The mouse is heavier.
   - ● The teddy is heavier.
   - ○ They are both the same.

2. Which has the smaller mass?
   - ● The sharpener
   - ○ The mouse

3. Which is true?
   - ○ The teddy is heavier.
   - ○ The cat is heavier.
   - ● They are both the same.

4. The ball has a bigger mass than the sharpener. Draw one at each end of the balance scale.
   Student drawing of ball at lower end and sharpener at higher end

5. Which is true?
   - ○ The white ball is much heavier.
   - ○ They have exactly the same mass.
   - ● They have almost the same mass.

6. Which is true?
   - ○ They have almost the same mass.
   - ● The pencil case is much heavier.

7. Which has about the same mass as a shoe?
   - ○ an eraser
   - ● a book
   - ○ a person
   - ○ a chair

8. Order the objects (A, B, C and D) from lightest to heaviest.
   A   B   C   D
   A D C B

87

172

OXFORD UNIVERSITY PRESS

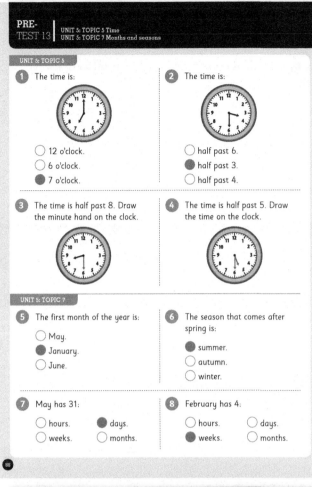

UNIT 5: TOPIC 5

1 The time is:
- ○ 12 o'clock.
- ○ 6 o'clock.
- ● 7 o'clock.

2 The time is:
- ○ half past 6.
- ● half past 3.
- ○ half past 4.

3 The time is half past 8. Draw the minute hand on the clock.

4 The time is half past 5. Draw the time on the clock.

UNIT 5: TOPIC 7

5 The first month of the year is:
- ○ May.
- ● January.
- ○ June.

6 The season that comes after spring is:
- ● summer.
- ○ autumn.
- ○ winter.

7 May has 31:
- ○ hours.
- ● days.
- ○ weeks.
- ○ months.

8 February has 4:
- ○ hours.
- ○ days.
- ● weeks.
- ○ months.

88

UNIT 5: TOPIC 5

1 At 3 o'clock the minute hand points to the:
- ○ 6 ● 12 ○ 3 ○ 9

2 The time is:
- ○ half past 6. ● half past 9.
- ○ half past 8.

3 The time is quarter past 10. Draw the minute hand on the clock.

4 The time is quarter to 4. Draw the time on the clock.

UNIT 5: TOPIC 7

5 The month that comes after April is:
- ● May. ○ March.
- ○ June.

6 Tran lives in Sydney. His birthday is in December. His birthday is in:
- ○ spring. ● summer.
- ○ autumn. ○ winter.

7 There are three months that begin with 'J'. Write the months in the order that they occur in the year.

January, June, July _____

_____

8 Look at question 6. Melbourne's winter months are:
- ○ April, May and June.
- ○ January, February and March.
- ● June, July and August.
- ○ August, September and October.

89

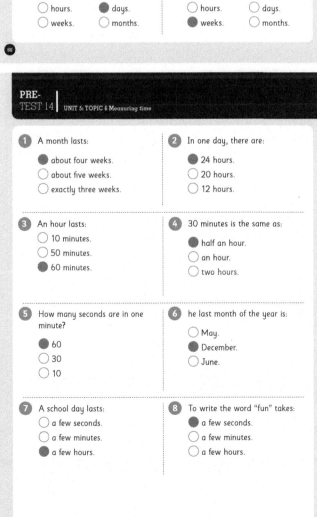

1 A month lasts:
- ● about four weeks.
- ○ about five weeks.
- ○ exactly three weeks.

2 In one day, there are:
- ● 24 hours.
- ○ 20 hours.
- ○ 12 hours.

3 An hour lasts:
- ○ 10 minutes.
- ○ 50 minutes.
- ● 60 minutes.

4 30 minutes is the same as:
- ● half an hour.
- ○ an hour.
- ○ two hours.

5 How many seconds are in one minute?
- ● 60
- ○ 30
- ○ 10

6 he last month of the year is:
- ○ May.
- ● December.
- ○ June.

7 A school day lasts:
- ○ a few seconds.
- ○ a few minutes.
- ● a few hours.

8 To write the word "fun" takes:
- ● a few seconds.
- ○ a few minutes.
- ○ a few hours.

90

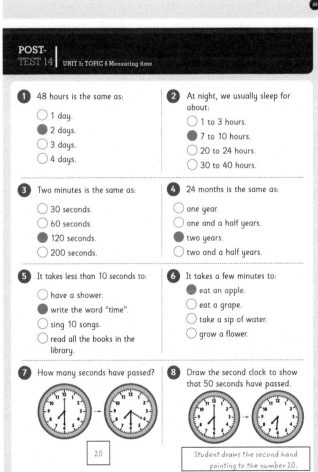

1 48 hours is the same as:
- ○ 1 day.
- ● 2 days.
- ○ 3 days.
- ○ 4 days.

2 At night, we usually sleep for about:
- ○ 1 to 3 hours.
- ● 7 to 10 hours.
- ○ 20 to 24 hours.
- ○ 30 to 40 hours.

3 Two minutes is the same as:
- ○ 30 seconds.
- ○ 60 seconds.
- ● 120 seconds.
- ○ 200 seconds.

4 24 months is the same as:
- ○ one year.
- ○ one and a half years.
- ● two years.
- ○ two and a half years.

5 It takes less than 10 seconds to:
- ○ have a shower.
- ● write the word "time".
- ○ sing 10 songs.
- ○ read all the books in the library.

6 It takes a few minutes to:
- ● eat an apple.
- ○ eat a grape.
- ○ take a sip of water.
- ○ grow a flower.

7 How many seconds have passed?

20

8 Draw the second clock to show that 50 seconds have passed.

Student draws the second hand pointing to the number 10.

91

PRE-TEST 15 | UNIT 5: TOPIC 8 Calendars

1 In a year, there are:
- ○ 7 months.
- ○ 10 months.
- ● 12 months.

2 What is the last month of the year?
- ○ May
- ○ January
- ● December
- ○ October

3 How many Saturdays are there in this month? Write the answer.

Sun	Mon	Tue	Wed	Thu	Fri	Sat
				1	2	3
4	5	6	7	8	9	10
11	12	13	14	15	16	17
18	19	20	21	22	23	24
25	26	27	28	29	30	31

5

4 Look at the calendar in question 3. On what day is the 12th?
- ○ Sunday
- ● Monday
- ○ Tuesday
- ○ Wednesday

5 Look at the calendar in question 3. What date is it a week after the 13th?
- ○ 19th
- ● 20th
- ○ 21st
- ○ 22nd

6 Look at the calendar in question 3. Three days after the 11th, the day is:
- ○ Monday.
- ○ Tuesday.
- ● Wednesday.
- ○ Thursday.

7 Look at the calendar in question 3. If this was the month of May, what date would it be the day after the 31st?

1st June

8 Look at the calendar in question 3. If this was the month of May, what date was the day before the 1st?

30th April

92

POST-TEST 15 | UNIT 5: TOPIC 8 Calendars

1 In January, there are:
- ○ 28 days.
- ○ 30 days.
- ● 31 days.

2 Could this calendar month be for June?

Sun	Mon	Tue	Wed	Thu	Fri	Sat
					1	2	3
4	5	6	7	8	9	10
11	12	13	14	15	16	17
18	19	20	21	22	23	24
25	26	27	28	29	30	31

○ Yes ● No

3 Which of these months have the same number of days?
- ○ March and April
- ○ April and May
- ○ May and June
- ● July and August

4 Look at the calendar in question 2. Which days are there five of in the month?
- ○ Monday, Tuesday, Wednesday
- ○ Wednesday, Thursday, Friday
- ● Thursday, Friday, Saturday
- ○ Friday, Saturday, Sunday

5 Which month never has more than 29 days?
- ● February
- ○ March
- ○ May
- ○ June

6 Look at the calendar in question 2. On what date is the first Wednesday of the month?

7th

7 Look at the calendar in question 2. If this was December, what was the date the day before December 1st?

30th November

8 Look at the calendar in question 2. If this was December, what would be the day and date 12 days after December 25th?

Friday, 6th January

93

PRE-TEST 16 | UNIT 6: TOPIC 1 2D shapes

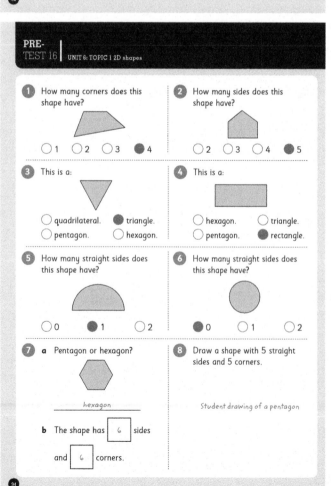

1 How many corners does this shape have?
- ○ 1 ○ 2 ○ 3 ● 4

2 How many sides does this shape have?
- ○ 2 ○ 3 ○ 4 ● 5

3 This is a:
- ○ quadrilateral.
- ● triangle.
- ○ pentagon.
- ○ hexagon.

4 This is a:
- ○ hexagon.
- ○ triangle.
- ○ pentagon.
- ● rectangle.

5 How many straight sides does this shape have?
- ○ 0 ● 1 ○ 2

6 How many straight sides does this shape have?
- ● 0 ○ 1 ○ 2

7 a Pentagon or hexagon?

hexagon

b The shape has 6 sides and 6 corners.

8 Draw a shape with 5 straight sides and 5 corners.

Student drawing of a pentagon

94

POST-TEST 16 | UNIT 6: TOPIC 1 2D shapes

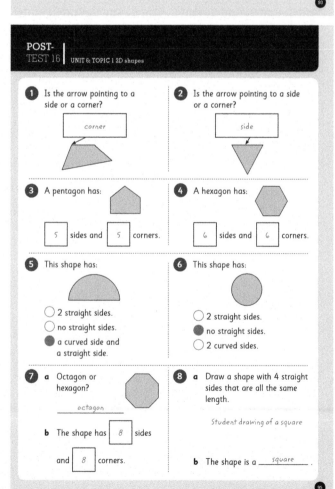

1 Is the arrow pointing to a side or a corner?

corner

2 Is the arrow pointing to a side or a corner?

side

3 A pentagon has:

5 sides and 5 corners.

4 A hexagon has:

6 sides and 6 corners.

5 This shape has:
- ○ 2 straight sides.
- ○ no straight sides.
- ● a curved side and a straight side.

6 This shape has:
- ○ 2 straight sides.
- ● no straight sides.
- ○ 2 curved sides.

7 a Octagon or hexagon?

octagon

b The shape has 8 sides and 8 corners.

8 a Draw a shape with 4 straight sides that are all the same length.

Student drawing of a square

b The shape is a ___square___.

95

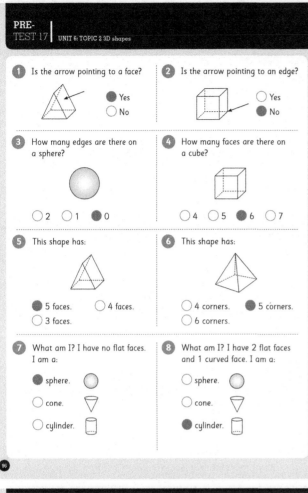

1 Is the arrow pointing to a face?
● Yes
○ No

2 Is the arrow pointing to an edge?
○ Yes
● No

3 How many edges are there on a sphere?
○ 2 ○ 1 ● 0

4 How many faces are there on a cube?
○ 4 ○ 5 ● 6 ○ 7

5 This shape has:
● 5 faces. ○ 4 faces.
○ 3 faces.

6 This shape has:
○ 4 corners. ● 5 corners.
○ 6 corners.

7 What am I? I have no flat faces. I am a:
● sphere.
○ cone.
○ cylinder.

8 What am I? I have 2 flat faces and 1 curved face. I am a:
○ sphere.
○ cone.
● cylinder.

96

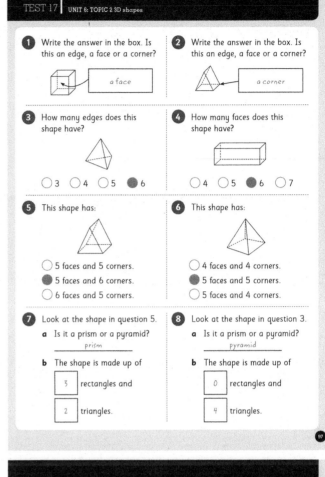

1 Write the answer in the box. Is this an edge, a face or a corner?
a face

2 Write the answer in the box. Is this an edge, a face or a corner?
a corner

3 How many edges does this shape have?
○ 3 ○ 4 ○ 5 ● 6

4 How many faces does this shape have?
○ 4 ○ 5 ● 6 ○ 7

5 This shape has:
○ 5 faces and 5 corners.
● 5 faces and 6 corners.
○ 6 faces and 5 corners.

6 This shape has:
○ 4 faces and 4 corners.
● 5 faces and 5 corners.
○ 5 faces and 4 corners.

7 Look at the shape in question 5.
a Is it a prism or a pyramid?
prism
b The shape is made up of
[3] rectangles and
[2] triangles.

8 Look at the shape in question 3.
a Is it a prism or a pyramid?
pyramid
b The shape is made up of
[0] rectangles and
[4] triangles.

97

---

1 Draw a star in the empty box on the bottom row.

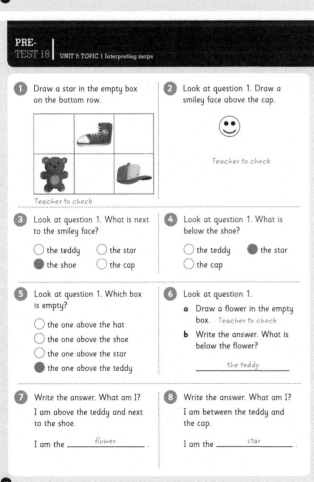

Teacher to check

2 Look at question 1. Draw a smiley face above the cap.

Teacher to check

3 Look at question 1. What is next to the smiley face?
○ the teddy ○ the star
● the shoe ○ the cap

4 Look at question 1. What is below the shoe?
○ the teddy ● the star
○ the cap

5 Look at question 1. Which box is empty?
○ the one above the hat
○ the one above the shoe
○ the one above the star
● the one above the teddy

6 Look at question 1.
a Draw a flower in the empty box. *Teacher to check*
b Write the answer. What is below the flower?
the teddy

7 Write the answer. What am I? I am above the teddy and next to the shoe.
I am the _flower_ .

8 Write the answer. What am I? I am between the teddy and the cap.
I am the _star_ .

98

---

1 Draw a star in the centre box.

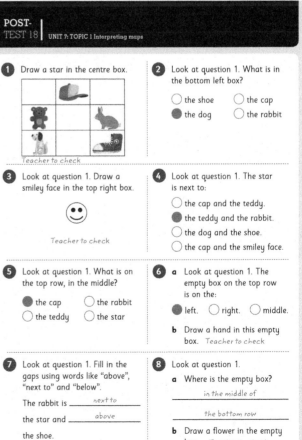

Teacher to check

2 Look at question 1. What is in the bottom left box?
○ the shoe ○ the cap
● the dog ○ the rabbit

3 Look at question 1. Draw a smiley face in the top right box.

Teacher to check

4 Look at question 1. The star is next to:
○ the cap and the teddy.
● the teddy and the rabbit.
○ the dog and the shoe.
○ the cap and the smiley face.

5 Look at question 1. What is on the top row, in the middle?
● the cap ○ the rabbit
○ the teddy ○ the star

6 a Look at question 1. The empty box on the top row is on the:
● left. ○ right. ○ middle.
b Draw a hand in this empty box. *Teacher to check*

7 Look at question 1. Fill in the gaps using words like "above", "next to" and "below".
The rabbit is _next to_
the star and _above_
the shoe.

8 Look at question 1.
a Where is the empty box?
in the middle of
the bottom row
b Draw a flower in the empty box. *Teacher to check*

99

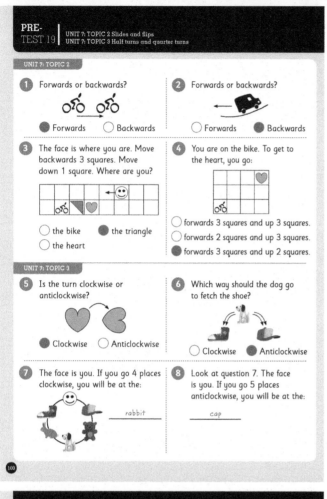

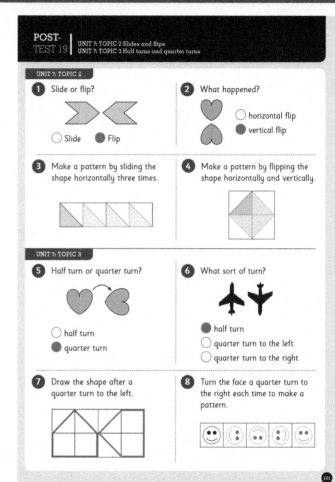

PRE-TEST 19 | UNIT 7: TOPIC 2 Slides and flips
UNIT 7: TOPIC 3 Half turns and quarter turns

UNIT 7: TOPIC 2

1. Forwards or backwards?
   ● Forwards   ○ Backwards

2. Forwards or backwards?
   ○ Forwards   ● Backwards

3. The face is where you are. Move backwards 3 squares. Move down 1 square. Where are you?
   ○ the bike   ● the triangle   ○ the heart

4. You are on the bike. To get to the heart, you go:
   ○ forwards 3 squares and up 3 squares.
   ○ forwards 2 squares and up 3 squares.
   ● forwards 3 squares and up 2 squares.

UNIT 7: TOPIC 3

5. Is the turn clockwise or anticlockwise?
   ● Clockwise   ○ Anticlockwise

6. Which way should the dog go to fetch the shoe?
   ○ Clockwise   ● Anticlockwise

7. The face is you. If you go 4 places clockwise, you will be at the:
   rabbit

8. Look at question 7. The face is you. If you go 5 places anticlockwise, you will be at the:
   cap

POST-TEST 19 | UNIT 7: TOPIC 2 Slides and flips
UNIT 7: TOPIC 3 Half turns and quarter turns

UNIT 7: TOPIC 2

1. Slide or flip?
   ○ Slide   ● Flip

2. What happened?
   ○ horizontal flip
   ● vertical flip

3. Make a pattern by sliding the shape horizontally three times.

4. Make a pattern by flipping the shape horizontally and vertically.

UNIT 7: TOPIC 3

5. Half turn or quarter turn?
   ○ half turn
   ● quarter turn

6. What sort of turn?
   ● half turn
   ○ quarter turn to the left
   ○ quarter turn to the right

7. Draw the shape after a quarter turn to the left.

8. Turn the face a quarter turn to the right each time to make a pattern.

PRE-TEST 20 | UNIT 8: TOPIC 1 Collecting data
UNIT 8: TOPIC 2 Collecting and classifying data
UNIT 8: TOPIC 3 Representing and interpreting data

1. Tran wrote a tick for each sticker he got. How many stickers did he get?
   ✓ ✓ ✓ ✓ ✓ ✓ ✓
   ○ 5   ○ 6   ● 7   ○ 8

2. Write a tick for every letter in the word "Wednesday".
   ✓ ✓ ✓ ✓ ✓ ✓ ✓ ✓ ✓

3. Tran wanted to know which pet people like. He asked 12 friends. The answers were:
   dog, dog, cat, dog, fish, cat, fish, dog, dog, cat, cat, dog
   Put a tick for each one.

Pet	Ticks
Dog	✓ ✓ ✓ ✓ ✓ ✓
Cat	✓ ✓ ✓ ✓
Fish	✓ ✓

4. Look at the data in question 3. Write the numbers in the table.

Pet	Total
Dog	6
Cat	4
Fish	2

5. Make a pictograph using the data in questions 3 and 4.

6. How many people like cats best?
   ○ 2   ○ 3   ● 4

7. How many more people chose dogs than fish?
   ○ 2   ○ 3   ● 4

8. What question do you think Tran asked the 12 people?
   Teacher to check

POST-TEST 20 | UNIT 8: TOPIC 1 Collecting data
UNIT 8: TOPIC 2 Collecting and classifying data
UNIT 8: TOPIC 3 Representing and interpreting data

1. Jack tallied the number of stickers he got. Fill in the totals.

Day	Tally	Total
Monday	III	3
Tuesday	IIII	5
Wednesday	IIII I	6
Thursday	IIII	4
Friday	III	3

2. Look at the table in question 1. The day Jack got the most stickers was:
   ○ Monday.   ○ Tuesday.
   ● Wednesday.   ○ Thursday.

3. Finish the graph for Tuesday.
   The number of stickers Jack got
   ☺ = 1 sticker

4. Finish the graph for Wednesday, Thursday and Friday.
   The number of stickers Jack got
   ☺ = 1 sticker

5. Look at the graphs. How many more stickers did Jack get on Wednesday than Monday?
   3

6. How many stickers did Jack get in the whole week?
   21

7. Next week, Jack will get 4 more stickers each day than he did the week before. Fill in the table.

Day	Tally	Total
Monday	IIII II	7
Tuesday	IIII IIII	9
Wednesday	IIII IIII	10
Thursday	IIII III	8
Friday	IIII II	7

8. Draw a pictograph using the data in question 7.
   The number of stickers Jack will get
   ☺ = 1 sticker

1 What is the chance that a cat will sit next to you in class today?

○ Certain ● Impossible

2 What is the chance that you will come to school next year?

● Certain ○ Impossible

3 What is the chance that it will rain next week?

○ Certain
● Maybe
○ Impossible

4 What is the chance that you will get all these questions right?

○ Certain
● Maybe
○ Impossible

5 Choose something that is **certain** to happen.

○ I will be on TV.
● I will read next week.
○ I will run from here to the Moon.

6 Choose something that is **impossible** to happen.

○ I will ride on a train one day.
● I will run around Australia backwards.
○ I will go to my friend's house.

7 What is something that might happen?

Teacher to check

_____
_____
_____
_____

8 What is something that will not happen?

Teacher to check

_____
_____
_____
_____

1 What is the chance that a pig will sing in class today?

○ Certain ● Impossible

2 What is the chance that someone will talk today?

● Certain ○ Impossible

3 What is the chance that the sun will shine next week?

○ Certain ● Likely
○ Unlikely ○ Impossible

4 What is the chance that you will get $100 at the weekend?

○ Certain ○ Likely
● Unlikely ○ Impossible

5 Choose the impossible event.

○ You will be famous.
○ You will become rich.
○ A dog will bark.
● A dog will grow wings and fly.

6 Choose the unlikely event.

○ You will smile next week.
○ You will read tomorrow.
● A dog will come into the classroom.
○ A dog will chase a cat.

7 What is something that is likely to happen?

Teacher to check

_____
_____
_____
_____
_____
_____

8 What is something that is unlikely to happen?

Teacher to check

_____
_____
_____
_____
_____
_____

ACTIVITY SHEETS
ANSWERS

Unit 1 Topic 1: Place value

Activity sheet 1: Sunshine and rainfall

1   a   8760
    b   4300

2   a   Yuma, Arizona
    b   Upington, South Africa and Atbara, Sudan
    c   3739, 3766, 3784, 4041, 4127
    d   3740

3

Place	Number of millimetres of rain in a year
Bellenden Ker Range	8636
Henderson Lake, Canada	6502
Quibdo, Colombia	8989
Dawei, Burma	5451
Kikori, Papua New Guinea	5916

Unit 1 Topic 2: Adding in your head

Activity sheet 2: What do you think?

1   Answers will vary. Teacher to check. Look for students who can accurately calculate to achieve solutions, and are able to use patterns and reasoning to generate different options. For example, 100 + 40 + 6, 100 + 41 + 5 and 100 + 42 + 4.

2   Answers will vary. Teacher to check. Look for students who offer a variety of accurate combinations to reach the given total.

3   Teacher to check. Look for the use of strategies such as the split strategy (80 + 80 + 8 + 6 = 160 + 14 = 174) or the bridging to a 10 strategy (88 + 2 + 84 = 90 + 84 = 174).

Unit 1 Topic 3: Exploring addition

Activity sheet 3: Selling chocolates

1   Students may have different number arrangements, e.g. Max: 54 + 46 +105 + 35, which is acceptable as long as they find the correct total.

Name	Week 1	Week 2	Week 3	Week 4	Best adding order	Total
Max	54	105	35	46	105 + 35 + 54 + 46	240
Conroy	78	61	102	139	139 + 61 + 102 + 78	380
Lottie	43	70	55	87	87 + 43 + 70 + 55	255
Boneka	60	54	86	40	60 + 40 + 86 + 54	240
Joey	36	82	91	62	36 + 82 + 62 + 91	271

2   Conroy
3   Max and Boneka

Unit 1 Topic 4: Subtracting in your head

Activity sheet 4: Subtraction race

This is a partner game. Allow students the opportunity to share the strategies they used for subtraction.

Unit 1 Topic 5: Exploring subtraction

Activity sheet 5: Eating chocolate

1   95 chocolate bars   2   63 chocolate bars
3   Austria and Russia   4   false

Unit 1 Topic 6: Multiplying

Activity sheet 6: Tim's Toyshop

1   a   30   b   50   c   80   d   100
2   a   16   b   12   c   20   d   18
3   a   4
    b   5
    c   10 × 2 = 20, 2 × 10 = 20, 20 × 1 = 20, 1 × 20 = 20
    d   six packs with two balls left over

Unit 1 Topic 7: Dividing

Activity sheet 7: Across the divide

1

Dividing by	Numbers that can be equally divided	Odd, even or both?
10	10, 20, 30	even
2	2, 4, 6, 8, 10, 12, 14, 16, 18, 20, 22, 24, 26, 28, 30	even
3	3, 6, 9, 12, 15, 18, 21, 24, 27, 30	both
4	4, 8, 12, 16, 20, 24, 28	even
5	5, 10, 15, 20, 25, 30	both
6	6, 12, 18, 24, 30	even

2   a   true   b   false   c   true   d   true   e   true
3   Teacher to check. Look for students who can draw on their calculations to demonstrate an understanding of how odd and even numbers work in division.

Unit 2 Topic 1: Fractions of objects

Activity sheet 8: Computer patterns

1   a–g   Teacher to check. Look for students who demonstrate an understanding of using a computer, and are able to make a fraction diagram based on the example provided.

(continued)

2 Teacher to check. Look for students who demonstrate an understanding of the concept of patterning, and can apply the directions from question 1 to make a fraction pattern.

3 Answers will vary. Teacher to check. Ensure that the fraction identified by students matches the fraction shaded in their patterns.

4 Answers will vary. Teacher to check. Look for students who are able to make a variety of fraction patterns, and can accurately describe the fractional parts they have shaded.

Unit 2 Topic 2: Fractions of groups

Activity sheet 9: Fraction mystery

1 a–k mothematics

2 Teacher to check. Look for students who can apply their understanding of unit fractions to create accurate clues for a mystery word.

Unit 3 Topic 1: Notes and coins

Activity sheet 10: International money

1 Answers will vary. Teacher to check.

2 Students' charts should contain the content in the table below, but the presentation may vary.

Coin or note	United States of America	New Zealand
1c coin	✓	✗
5c coin	✓	✗
10c coin	✓	✓
20c coin	✗	✓
25c coin	✓	✗
50c coin	✓	✓
$1 coin	✓	✓
$2 coin	✓	✓
$1 note	✓	✗
$2 note	✓	✗
$5 note	✓	✓
$10 note	✓	✓
$20 note	✓	✓
$50 note	✓	✓
$100 note	✓	✓

3 a 50 **b** 100 **c** 150 **d** 1000
   e 500 **f** 5000

Unit 3 Topic 2: Counting money

Activity sheet 11: Money transactions

1 a Multiple answers possible. Teacher to check. Look for students who show fluency with addition and sound reasoning by being able to suggest a variety of combinations.
   b $7.50 **c** $22.50 **d** $27.50

2 a $5 **b** $5 **c** $10 **d** $20

3 a 40 **b** 20 **c** 80

4 Multiple answers possible. Teacher to check. Look for students who are able to identify more than one answer from the following, and can demonstrate their problem solving, reasoning and fluency with number by using systematic methods to identify the possible answers.

   2 × $20 notes; 4 × $10 notes; 8 × $5 notes; 1 × $20 note and 2 × $10 notes; 1 × $20 note and 4 × $5 notes; 1 × $20 note, 1 × $10 note and 2 × $5 notes; 3 × $10 notes and 2 × $5 notes; 2 × $10 notes and 4 × $5 notes; 1 × $10 note and 6 × $5 notes.

5 a $6.85
   b 2 × $2 coins, 2 × $1 coins and 2 × 50c coins
   c 1 × 10c coin and 1 × 5c coin or 3 × 5c coins

6 a $18.20 **b** $9.10 **c** 90c **d** $4.40

7 Teacher to check. Look for students who can correctly interpret the problem and fluently add money amounts to stay within the given total.

Unit 4 Topic 1: Describing patterns

Activity sheet 12: Finding patterns

1 a It's a repeating pattern of four pale-grey marbles and one dark-grey marble. Students may express this in different ways. Any answer that accurately describes the pattern is acceptable.
   b The next five marbles should be: pale grey, pale grey, pale grey, pale grey, dark grey.

2 a 4
   b Bigger – the smaller fish appears in positions 4, 8, 12 and 16, so position 15 must be bigger.
   c Smaller – the smaller fish appears in every fourth position: 4, 8, 12, 16, 20 and 24.
   d The 36th fish should be a smaller fish.

3 a Every 10th teddy bear has a hat.
   b Every 5th teddy bear is holding a heart.
   c No – 53 is not in the fives counting pattern.
   d Yes – 50 is in the tens counting pattern.
   e The teddy bear should be holding a heart.
   f The teddy bear should be holding a heart and wearing a hat.

4 a & b Teacher to check. Look for students who show a solid understanding of the concept of patterning and are able to accurately create and describe their own pattern.

Unit 4 Topic 2: Number sentences

Activity sheet 13: Computer problem solving

1

	A	B
1	Packs	Cup cakes
2	15	75

2 Teacher to check. Look for students who have correctly set up their spreadsheets as per the image in question 1 above, and can use the spreadsheet to make calculations using different numbers.

3 **a** 14 **b** 42 **c** 84 **d** 126

Unit 5 Topic 1: Length and area

Activity sheet 14: Bedroom decorating

1 **a** Teacher to check. Look for students who understand the concept of perimeter and are able to correctly outline an area with the given perimeter on their grid paper.
  b 60 squares

2 **a & b** Teacher to check. Look for students who are able to use their problem-solving skills to correctly interpret the requirements of the problem, and who are able to accurately calculate area using squares as a uniform informal unit.

3 **a & b** Teacher to check. Look for students who can use their understanding of area to create a room, and accurately represent the area of the total room and the used floor space in squares.

Unit 5 Topic 2: Metres and centimetres

Activity sheet 15: Small dinosaurs

1 **a**

Name	Length
micropachycephalosaurus	50 cm
saltopus	59 cm
yandagornis	60 cm
bambiraptor	69 cm
microraptor	77 cm

  b 23 cm
  c Teacher to check. Look for students who are able to accurately measure and record the length of the word in centimetres.
  d 27 cm
  e 315 cm
  f Teacher to check. Look for students who are able to use their problem-solving skills to find their own height, and who can then accurately calculate the difference between their height and 50 cm.

Unit 5 Topic 3: Volume and capacity

Activity sheet 16: Make a container

1 **a & b** Teacher to check. Look for students who understand the concept of stacking items in equal layers, and can use their problem-solving and reasoning skills to make a box of the appropriate volume.

2 **a** No – it's a different shape.
  b Teacher to check. Look for students who are able to successfully make a container that will hold their new arrangement of blocks.

3 Teacher to check. Look for students who use methods such as flattening the boxes to make direct comparisons, or who use uniform informal units to make a well-reasoned comparison of the two areas.

Unit 5 Topic 4: Mass

Activity sheet 17: Heaviest and lightest animals

1 **a** giant Flemish rabbit, goliath beetle, St Bernard
  b 115 kg
  c Less than half a kilogram – half a kilogram is the same as 500 g and the goliath beetle has a mass of only 100 g.
  d 600 kg

2 **a** $\frac{1}{2}$ g, 3 g, 110 g, 500 g, 600 g
  b dwarf Dutch rabbit, chihuahua
  c 107 g
  d 10

Unit 5 Topic 5: Time

Activity sheet 18: A day out

1 **a** 5 past 6 or 6:05
  b 20 minutes
  c There are 60 seconds in a minute.
  d 12 minutes past 6 or 6:12
  e seven minutes

2 **a** 19 minutes past 6 or 6:19
  b 120 seconds

3 **a** about quarter past 7
  b 39 minutes past 7 or 7:39
  c 34 minutes past 7 or 7:34

4 5 past 8 or 8:05

5 28 minutes past 9 or 9:28

6 **a** 25 to 10 or 9:35
  b three hours and 30 minutes

7 **a** 5 to 10 or 9:55
  b 15 minutes
  c 10 past 10 or 10:10

8 eight hours

9 Teacher to check. Look for students who can represent and interpret time to the minute, and can make reasonable estimates of the duration of common events.

Unit 5 Topic 7: Months and seasons

Activity sheet 19: What season is it?

1 Canada – northern hemisphere
   France – northern hemisphere
   Fiji – southern hemisphere
   Egypt – northern hemisphere
   India – northern hemisphere
   Madagascar – southern hemisphere
   Tonga – southern hemisphere
   Japan – northern hemisphere
   Nauru – southern hemisphere
   United States of America – northern hemisphere

2

Country	Month	Season
Madagascar	August	winter
United States of America	June	summer
India	December	winter
Japan	March	spring
Nauru	March	autumn
France	January	winter
Egypt	October	autumn

3 a Teacher to check. Look for students who recognise
      that the Earth's tilt results in it being warmer or
      cooler at different parts of the year, depending on
      its position in relation to the Sun.
   b Teacher to check. Look for students who understand
      that the Earth's tilt also means that the northern
      hemisphere is closer to the Sun when the southern
      hemisphere is tilted away, and vice versa.

Unit 5 Topic 8: Calendars

Activity sheet 20: Day-of-year calendars

1 a 1   b 61   c 60   d 20   e 77   f 121

2 There will be 366 days because 2016 is a leap year with
   29 days in February.

3 a 122   b 366   c 360

4 The first day of the day-of-year calendar year is the
   same as the first day of the traditional calendar year,
   and therefore the dates in January and the numbers
   in the day-of-year calendar align.

5 Teacher to check. Look for students who can accurately
   use a day-of-year calendar to find the correct number
   for their birthday.

6

Month	Normal year Day number range	Leap year Day number range
January	1–31	1–31
February	32–59	32–60
March	60–90	61–91
April	91–120	92–121
May	121–151	122–152
June	152–181	153–182
July	182–212	183–213
August	213–243	214–244
September	244–273	245–274
October	274–304	275–305
November	305–334	306–335
December	335–365	336–366

(continued)

7 Note: Non-leap year example shown below. For a leap year, add one day to February and then increase the day numbers in each subsequent month by one.

Date	Jan	Feb	Mar	Apr	May	Jun	Jul	Aug	Sep	Oct	Nov	Dec
1	1	32	60	91	121	152	182	213	244	274	305	335
2	2	33	61	92	122	153	183	214	245	275	306	336
3	3	34	62	93	123	154	184	215	246	276	307	337
4	4	35	63	94	124	155	185	216	247	277	308	338
5	5	36	64	95	125	156	186	217	248	278	309	339
6	6	37	65	96	126	157	187	218	249	279	310	340
7	7	38	66	97	127	158	188	219	250	280	311	341
8	8	39	67	98	128	159	189	220	251	281	312	342
9	9	40	68	99	129	160	190	221	252	282	313	343
10	10	41	69	100	130	161	191	222	253	283	314	344
11	11	42	70	101	131	162	192	223	254	284	315	345
12	12	43	71	102	132	163	193	224	255	285	316	346
13	13	44	72	103	133	164	194	225	256	286	317	347
14	14	45	73	104	134	165	195	226	257	287	318	348
15	15	46	74	105	135	166	196	227	258	288	319	349
16	16	47	75	106	136	167	197	228	259	289	320	350
17	17	48	76	107	137	168	198	229	260	290	321	351
18	18	49	77	108	138	169	199	230	261	291	322	352
19	19	50	78	109	139	170	200	231	262	292	323	353
20	20	51	79	110	140	171	201	232	263	293	324	354
21	21	52	80	111	141	172	202	233	264	294	325	355
22	22	53	81	112	142	173	203	234	265	295	326	356
23	23	54	82	113	143	174	204	235	266	296	327	357
24	24	55	83	114	144	175	205	236	267	297	328	358
25	25	56	84	115	145	176	206	2237	268	298	329	359
26	26	57	85	116	146	177	207	238	269	299	330	360
27	27	58	86	117	147	178	208	239	270	300	331	361
28	28	59	87	118	148	179	209	240	271	301	332	362
29	29		88	119	149	180	210	241	272	302	333	363
30	30		89	120	150	181	211	242	273	303	334	364
31	31		90		151		212	243		304		365

8 **a** 1 (leap year or non-leap year)
   b 45 (leap year or non-leap year)
   c 359 (or 360 in a leap year)

OXFORD UNIVERSITY PRESS

Unit 6 Topic 1: 2D shapes

Activity sheet 21: Shape patterns

1 a–h Teacher to check. Look for students who can follow the directions accurately, and who have created a 5-square pattern that meets the specifications.

2 a–d Teacher to check. Look for students who are able to use software to create patterns with the given shapes. Students may identify that rectangles, triangles and regular hexagons tessellate, whereas regular pentagons do not tessellate. Students might also discover that some irregular pentagons can tessellate, or that combinations of shapes such as pentagons and stars or diamonds also tessellate.

3 a & b Teacher to check. Look for students who can successfully join different shapes and accurately identify the resultant polygons.

Unit 6 Topic 2: 3D shapes

Activity sheet 22: Which object is that?

1 Responses will vary. Teacher to check. Some examples include a ball (sphere), a tissue box (rectangular prism), a paint can (cylinder), a tent (triangular prism), the Louvre (pyramid).

2 triangular prism; square pyramid; rectangular prism

3 Teacher to check. Look for students who show a sound understanding of the features of 3D shapes, and who are able to use reasoning to identify similarities and differences. This might include comparing the number and shape of the faces, the names of the shapes or other attributes, such as whether or not the shapes can roll.

Unit 7 Topic 1: Interpreting maps

Activity sheet 23: Treasure Island

1 a–g

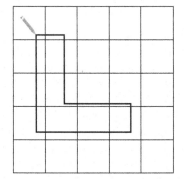

D = Deadly snake
P = Poisonous spider
G = Glass spikes
R = Razor wire
B = Bomb
H = Hand crusher

h The key is behind the bottom left-hand door.

2 a E4
   b C3

c–g

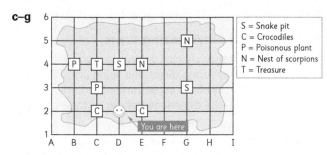

S = Snake pit
C = Crocodiles
P = Poisonous plant
N = Nest of scorpions
T = Treasure

h C4

3 a & b Teacher to check. Look for students who can follow the instructions to find a path along the grid lines to the treasure, and use the language of direction to describe the route that they took.

Unit 7 Topic 2: Slides and flips

Activity sheet 24: Sliding around

1 a The puppy's location has changed. All aspects of the puppy's appearance have remained the same.
   b Answers may vary. Teacher to check. Examples: "Slide up three squares. Then slide left one square." "Slide left one square. Then slide up three squares."

2 a The diagonal slide is more direct and, therefore, faster.
   b Answers may vary. Teacher to check. Example: "Slide up three squares and left one square."

3 a–g

4 a–d Teacher to check. Look for students who are able to apply their knowledge of sliding movements to write accurate directions that match the letter they have drawn on the grid.

Unit 7 Topic 3: Half turns and quarter turns

Activity sheet 25: Amazing turns

1 **a & b** Teacher to check. Look for students who can write accurate directions using clockwise and anticlockwise quarter turns, and can successfully follow the directions written by their partner.

   c 43

2 **a–c** Teacher to check. Look for students who are able to apply their knowledge of quarter turns when creating their maze, and can describe the directions they take to complete a maze using the language of direction.

Unit 8 Topic 1: Collecting data

Activity sheet 26: Popular names

1 **a & b**

Position	Name	Tally marks	Number of letters
1st	Isabella	ЖЖ |||	8
2nd	Ruby	||||	4
3rd	Chloe	ЖЖ	5
4th	Olivia	ЖЖ		6
5th	Charlotte	ЖЖ ||||	9
6th	Mia	|||	3
7th	Lily	||||	4
8th	Emily	ЖЖ	5
9th	Ella	||||	4
10th	Sienna	ЖЖ		6

   c Charlotte – nine letters

   d Answers will vary depending on the students' names.

   e Answers will vary. Teacher to check. Look for students who understand the concept of difference between, and who are able to accurately interpret the data to calculate the difference between the number of letters in the longest name on the list and their own.

2 **a–f** Teacher to check. Look for students who are able to accurately represent the data they collect using tally marks, and show fluency in totalling and comparing the numbers of letters in the names.

3 **a & b** Answers will vary. Teacher to check. Look for students who use sound reasoning to support their responses.

   c Answers will vary. Teacher to check. Likely response is, "What is your favourite name on this list?" But accept any variation that will result in the collection of appropriate data.

   d Teacher to check. Look for students who use effective data collection and recording practices and make an accurate record of their findings.

Unit 8 Topic 2: Collecting and classifying data

Activity sheet 27: Keeping track of information

1 **a**

Number of letters in word	3	4	5	6	7	8	9
Tally	||||	|||	|||	|||	||	||||		
Total	4	3	3	3	2	4	1

   b four

   c seventeen

   d two

2 Teacher to check. Look for students who are able to set up a frequency table and can accurately keep track of data using effective data collection methods.

3 **a–c** Teacher to check. Look for students who can write a yes/no question and demonstrate an understanding of the possible results that their question will yield with different groups of people.

4 **a–d** Teacher to check. Look for students who can identify and structure a plausible question, and can use reasoning to justify why the results were or were not as predicted.

5 **a–e** Teacher to check. Look for students who can use their knowledge of questioning and data collection to conduct a survey and to make reasonable deductions based on their results.

Unit 8 Topic 3: Representing and interpreting data

Activity sheet 28: The world's tallest

1 **a** China

   b three

   c China

   d USA

2 **a** one

   b China

   c one

   d the height of the buildings

3 Teacher to check. Look for students who can construct an accurate pictograph based on the given data.

4 **a–h**

France	1
Russia	1
China	4
Japan	1
South Korea	1
Hong Kong	1
Denmark	1

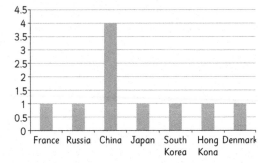

(continued)

5 Teacher to check. Look for students whose chart accurately represents the data that they were presented with.

6 **a–c** Teacher to check. Look for students who choose an appropriate way to represent their data, and whose data display accurately represents the data they collected.

Unit 9 Topic 1: Chance

Activity sheet 29: What's on for the weekend?

1 Teacher to check. Look for students who choose appropriate alternatives, such as playing netball or sleeping.

2 Teacher to check. Look for students who choose appropriate alternatives, such as playing sport.

3 Answers may vary depending on students' opinions and experiences. Accept alternatives to the suggested responses below if students can provide adequate reasoning for their choices.

   a Equal chance – neither Evie nor Taj have indicated whether they like or dislike shopping, and either may be required to go with their parents.

   b Evie is more likely to go running because Taj dislikes sport.

   c Taj is more likely to go to a cartooning workshop because he has an interest in art.

   d Equal chance – we don't know whether or not either Evie or Taj like pizza so there is no reason to think one is more likely than the other to eat it on the weekend.

4 Answers may vary depending on students' perspectives. Accept alternatives to the suggested responses below if students can provide adequate reasoning for their choices.

   a likely
   b unlikely
   c possible
   d possible
   e equal chance
   f impossible
   g certain

Teacher notes

Teacher notes

Teacher notes